MINISTERO PER I BENI E LE ATTIVITÀ CULTURALI
SOPRINTENDENZA ARCHEOLOGICA DI ROMA

MUSEO NAZIONALE ROMANO
THE BATHS OF DIOCLETIAN

Maria A. Liston
18 May 2002
Rome

ELECTA

Cover illustration
The Inside of the Octagonal
Hall with the bronze statue
of the Hellenistic Prince

Translation
Greg Bailey

Texts by
Anna Maria Bietti Sestieri [AMBS]
Anna De Santis [ADS]
Rosanna Friggeri [RF]
Marina Magnani Cianetti [MMC]
Nicoletta Pagliardi [NP]
Gianluca Tagliamonte [GT]

CONTENTS

THE BATHS
OF DIOCLETIAN

FROM THE THERMAE FELICES
TO THE MUSEUM

The Baths of Diocletian (*Thermae Diocletianae*) rose up in the sixth (*Alta Semita* by name) of the fourteen *regiones* into which Augustus had subdivided the city of Rome. They were situated on the plateau at the eastern end of the Quirinal and the Viminal hills, near one of the most densely populated areas of ancient Rome; it was in fact the need to provide the crowded neighborhoods on the slopes of the Quirinal and Viminal with a monumental bathing establishment which determined the site of the city's largest *thermae*.

Before beginning the construction work on the Baths, the Imperial administration first had to expropriate and then demolish the numerous private buildings which crowded the zone (as is recorded in the dedicatory inscription: *coemptis aedificiis pro tanti operis magnitudine*) together with the public buildings and other structures present. A good many buildings and monuments must have been destroyed to clear the space for the grandiose new construction, although we have traces of only a few in archeological documentation or literary sources.

Among these was certainly the *domus* of *Cornelia L(uci) f(ilia) Volusi Saturnini praefecti*, a noblewoman of the Augustan age—we have the evi-

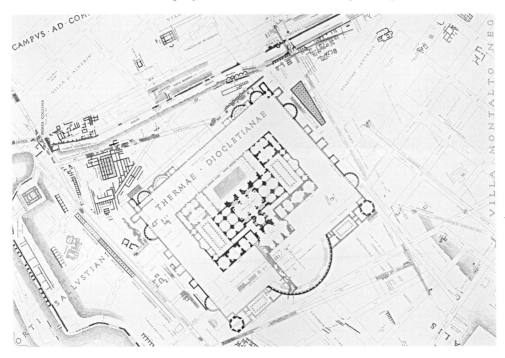

Dedicatory inscription of the Baths of Diocletian

[D(omini)] n(ostri) [D]iocletia[nus]
et [Maximia]nus Invicti /
senio[res Aug(usti), patres Imp(eratorum)
et Ca]es(arum), et /
d(omini) n(ostri) Cons[tantius et Maximianus
invicti Aug(usti) et /
Severus et] Max[iminus nobilissimi Caesares /
ther]mas feli[ces Dio]cletianas, quas /
[M]aximianus Aug(ustus) [redien]s ex Africa sub /
praesentia ma[iestatis] disposuit ac /
[f]ieri iussit et Diocletiani Aug(usti) fratris sui /
nomini consecravit [coemptis aedifici]is /
[pro] ta[nti oper]is magni[tudine omni c]ultu /
perfec[tas] Romanis sui[s] dedic[ave]ru[nt]

"Our invincible lords, the elder Augusti Diocletian and Maximian, fathers of the Emperors and of the Caesars, and our invincible lords Constantius and Maximian, Augusti, and Severus and Maximin, noblest Caesars, have dedicated to their Romans these auspicious Baths of Diocletian, which Maximian Augustus ordered to be built upon his return from Africa in the presence of His Majesty, and which he consecrated in the name of his brother Diocletian, having acquired the premises requisite to a work of such grandeur, and sumptuously fitting them out in every detail"

dence in a *fistula aquaria* (*CIL* XV, 7441), or inscribed water main, excavated from under the large exedra of the Baths. That the area contained private residences, and that some of these were quite luxurious, is also demonstrated by a number of houses apparently demolished when the foundations were laid for the *thermae*, discovered in the precinct at the end of the nineteenth century, and, more recently, during the excavations carried out in Piazza della Repubblica in 1965 and 1969 for the construction of the A Line of the Rome subway. In particular, the structures brought to light in 1969 seem to belong to two buildings, or, perhaps, to two successive construction phases (the older of the two datable to the beginning of the Imperial age) of one large complex, characterized by the presence of curious mixed-line structures which remain difficult to interpret.

Along with the private dwellings, a number of *tabernae*, cisterns, and other structures were demolished; remains of some of these were discovered during the excavations in the final decades of the nineteenth century occasioned by the urbanization of the area between Via XX Settembre and Termini train station.

The *Historia Augusta* (*Thirty Tyrants,* 21, 3-7) describes a monument called the *quadrigae Pisonis,* composed of several triumphal chariots and a statue erected by the Senate in honor of *(Calpurnius) Piso Frugi,* governor of Tessaglia under Gallienus, and one of the thirty tyrants.

It is also possible that the Temple of the *Gens Flavia,* which was built on the site of the *domus* of Vespasian's brother, *Titus Flavius Sabinus,* where Domitian was born, was demolished during the construction of the Baths. D. Candilio has recently suggested that the remnants uncovered at different sites in the sector bounded by Via Parigi, Via Vittorio Emanuele Orlando, and the church of San Bernardo should be identified with this earlier structure.

The late Imperial upgrading of the neighborhood also included a more efficient layout of the streets; the northeast stretch of the *vicus Longus* was eliminated (it ran in the valley between the Quirinal and the Viminal, along the lines of the present-day Via Nazionale), while a new transversal street joined the two main arteries which ran in an east-west direction along the summits of the two hills (respectively, the *Alta Semita,* or the present-day Via Quirinale and Via XX Settembre; and the *vi-*

cus Collis Viminalis, part of whose course retraced the Via Viminale).
Once the area had been cleared of the earlier constructions, the site was
filled in and leveled. On the basis of indications provided by the more
recent studies and test digs conducted in the area of the Baths, it seems
that the builders generally left the pre-existent structures (leveled as necessary) which did not interfere with the foundations of the new buildings. At this point they could then proceed with the actual construction
of the thermal complex.

A dedicatory inscription discovered in the zone of the Baths of Diocletian (*CIL* VI, 1130 = 31242), of which there must have existed several
copies, provides useful information as to the commencement and duration of construction. Even in its fragmentary state, the text can easily be
reconstituted in whole with the help of a transcription by the Anonymous Einsiedlensis, author of an *itinerarium* of Rome which appeared in
the late eighth or early ninth century. He could see one of the inscriptions almost intact.

Maximian had gone to Africa to subdue the Quinquegentiani rebellion,
and returned to Rome in the autumn of AD 298. The indications contained in the inscription, then, allow us to affirm that the construction
work on the Baths, undertaken in the name of his elder colleague Diocletian, started at this time and continued for seven to eight years, given
that they were completed after the abdication of Diocletian and Maximian in favor of Galerius Maximian and Constance Chlore (May 1, AD
305), but before the death of the latter (July 25, AD 306). This dating
is, in addition, confirmed by the brick stamps from the Baths: they are
all, in fact, ascribable to Diocletian's reign, in particular to the years AD
292-305.

The bath complex occupied a precinct of over 13.5 hectares, corresponding to a vast area which today stretches out between the Via Torino, Via del Viminale, Piazza dei Cinquecento, Via Volturno, and Via XX
Settembre. The *thermae* reproduced the by-then canonical plan for Im-

*4. The Baths
of Diocletian in the
architect Italo Gismondi's
scale model of Rome
in the age of
Constantine. Rome,
Museo della Civiltà
Romana*

perial baths, derived from the Baths of Trajan and reproduced as well in the Baths of Caracalla. Curiously, these three *thermae* are disposed along an almost perfectly oriented North-South axis which runs through the city, and at very nearly equal distances from each other.

The plan of the Baths of Diocletian is rather easily reconstructible in spite of the serious destruction and the numerous transformations which the remaining structures have suffered through the course of the centuries; it consists of a large outer precinct wall enclosing a vast open area, in the center of which rose the actual bath building.

The outer wall roughly defined a rectangle of 376 by 361 meters. The principal entrance (1), in the center of the northeast side (parallel to Via Volturno, more or less along the axis of the present-day Via Montebello), was flanked on either side by symmetrically disposed spaces, among which were four large semicircular apses (two on each side), decorated with columns and niches (2a, b; 3a, b).

Six spaces symmetrically articulated each of the longer sides (those northwest and southeast). One of these functioned as the secondary entrance to the complex (4a, b); of the remaining five rooms, the two larger ones were semicircular, and the other three rectangular in plan.

The fourth precinct wall, that on the southwest side, had an enormous exedra in the center (5), furnished with rows of stepped benches, and decorated with a series of columned *aediculae*, which was perhaps used for theatrical performances. The outline of this exedra is reproduced, in a slightly reduced form, in the present Piazza della Repubblica (formerly Piazza dell'Esedra). The exedra was flanked by two rectangular halls (6a, b), reasonably recognizable as libraries, and probably the same ones, according to the *Historia Augusta* (*Life of Probus*, 2,1), into which were transferred the books once conserved in Trajan's Forum and in the library of the *Domus Tiberiana*. These were followed by several small spaces and, in the extremities, in correspondence with the angles of the outer wall, two circular halls, or rotundas (7a, b), with four entrances arranged in a cross, alternating with four small semicircular niches.

A large esplanade spread beyond the entrance (or, more accurately, entrances) of the precinct walls, laid out for the most part with gardens (*xysti*: 8), and embellished with statues, shrines, *nymphea*, and other small structures. We have additional evidence for this in the sixteenth-century descriptions of the Baths left to us by Bartolomeo Marliano and Ulisse Aldrovandi.

The bath hall was placed in the middle of the esplanade, measuring some 250 by 180 meters. The canonical plan provided for the distribution of the principal spaces, the bathing ones properly speaking, along the short central axis: first, the grand swimming pool of the *natatio*, with a total area around 2500 square meters (9), bordered on its shorter sides by porticos, and on the southeast by an imposing architectonic façade; the *frigidarium* (also known as the "basilica:" 10), composed of a magnificent hall covered with a triple cross vault, into which opened four smaller spaces with large bathing pools for cold baths; the *tepidarium* (11), a dome-covered circular room with two large rectangular exedrae and four small lateral niches; and, finally, the *caldarium* (12), a rectangular hall covered with a triple cross vault and extended on either end by an apse containing a bathing pool.

* The numbers in parenthesis in this chapter refer to the numbers indicated in in the plan on the next page.

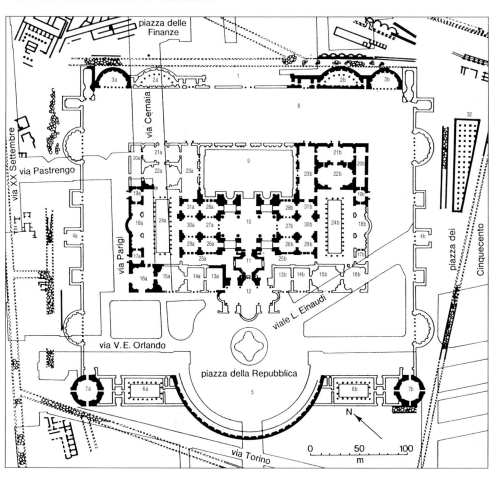

A number of other spaces were arranged symmetrically in the lateral wings of the complex around two porticoed rectangular exercise yards (*palaestrae*: 24a, b), onto which opened a series of interconnecting halls (18a, b), including the central one with apses. It is not possible to positively assign a precise function to these rooms, but we can reasonably identify some of these accessory spaces with the names which have been handed down to us by literary and epigraphic sources—for example, *destrictarium, unctorium, conisterium*, etc.

Two double-apsed halls (probably *apodyteria*, or dressing rooms: 22a, b) were situated among these rooms, one on either side of the *natatio*, and both proceeded by rectangular vestibules (21a, b). On either side of the *frigidarium* was a complex of six rooms arranged in two symmetrical rows of three (26a, b-31a, b). A long service hallway (25a, b) ran between the *frigidarium* and the *caldarium* at a lower level than that of the surrounding rooms, with stairs and access to the basement. Finally, a line of three rectangular rooms extended perpendicularly on either side of the *caldarium* (13a, b-15a, b), which were also floored with *suspensurae*, and therefore heated; beyond these followed two rooms (16a, b) ensconced in the corners of the main building which served as secondary *frigidaria*, each rectangular on the outside and octagonal within.

5. Reconstructed plan of the complex of the Baths of Diocletian; surrounding it are the ancient buildings brought to light during the course of the excavations and construction projects of the past years

The Baths of Diocletian were the largest bath complex in ancient Rome. A passage of Olympodorus of Thebes, related by Fotius (80, p. 63, Bekker), suggests that they could be used simultaneously by some 3000 individuals, which is almost double the capacity of the Baths of Caracalla. The reliability of this particular piece of evidence, however, is far from universally accepted.

The Baths were constructed of concrete poured into a well-engineered brick shell which was reinforced at stress points with *bipedali*, two-foot-square bricks. *Bipedali* were also used to form the arches of the doors, windows, and niches, those supporting the floors in the heated rooms, and the vaulting of the drainage system. (Remains of drainage pipes and a cryptoportico were brought to light in the previously-mentioned 1969 excavations.) The heating system used is known as the hypocaust; hot air circulated under a floor, the *suspensura*, suspended on piles of bricks, and around the walls, through hollow terracotta tubes (*tubuli*).

The vaults were formed by a brick skeleton and concrete composed of lime with *tufo* and pumice fragments to lighten the load. Windows of various sizes (some enormous) and open skylights (*oculi*) provided light and, to a certain extent, heat, to the various rooms of the complex.

We can get an idea of the richness of the interior and exterior decoration of the building not only from the archeological evidence, but also thanks to a vast graphic documentation (drawings and etchings) which goes back to the late fifteenth century.

The walls were faced on the outside with marble slabs, at least up to a certain height; above this height the decoration often continued in stucco painted in *faux* marble compositions. The bathing pools were also lined with marble on the bottom and sides; recent restoration and reconstruction work on the underground rooms of the museum revealed remains of the pavement and walls of the *natatio*, with traces of a huge drain hole. The various niches which animated the surfaces of the rooms were also covered with marble. Certain ceilings and niche vaults show evidence of being decorated in glass mosaic, often gilded.

At the end of the sixteenth century, frescoes were still visible in the rooms transformed into the *casino* of the *Horti Belleiani*, located in the middle of the great exedra on the southwest side. These were declared "obscene" by Caterina Nobili Sforza, who had them destroyed, but are probably the same compositions reproduced in a drawing by Baldassarre Peruzzi.

The decoration extended to the floors as well; these were set with large mosaic compositions known to us in part through remains dug up in various places during the last few centuries, as well as through graphic documentation. Among those still preserved today are the black-and-white floor mosaic of the large apsed semicircular hall on the northeast side of the outer wall (2b), and the fragment discovered during the course of test digs conducted in the 1980s in the area between Via Cernaia, Santa Maria degli Angeli, the access ramp to the sacristy of the church, and the buildings of the former *Magistero*. In these latter structures, which correspond to a part of the peristyle and central court of the northwest gymnasium (*palaestra*) of the Baths (24a), archeologists found substantial traces of a polychrome geometric composition, realized in large *tesserae* of white marble, *giallo antico*, green serpentine, and red porphyry. Fragments of this type of flooring have come to light in Hall VIII (fig. 3, bay 23b).

We have significant vestiges of the original architectonic decoration—

especially inside the basilica of Santa Maria degli Angeli, with its eight enormous monolithic columns in pink granite, and capitals and trabeation in marble (10)—but also in the church ("rotunda") of San Bernardo, with its impressive dome articulated with octagonal coffers (7a), and in the octagonal hall, where travertine brackets constitute the inner framework of the tympanum cornice (16a). We also have an abundance of architectonic fragments (cornices, brackets, capitals, and bits of architrave) recovered from the site but no longer in place, in various marbles (*lunense*, pentelic and proconnesian), some of which are recycled elements predating the age of Diocletian.

The decoration of the façade of the *natatio* (9) was particularly ornate, and was depicted in numerous prints and drawings from the Renaissance on, although only a small part is left today. The monumental and quite animated elevation was articulated in five bays (three rectangular ones alternating with two semicircular ones, in an ABABA rhythm), separated by pairs of projecting columns, Ionic on the lower order, and Corinthian on the upper. The bays contained three orders of tabernacle niches designed to house statues, with richly sculpted cornices and admirable brackets figuring eagles holding a thunderbolt.

Not much can be said about the sculptural decoration in the building, which, however, must have been equally rich. As far as the interior of the building is concerned, it is reasonable to assume that the sculpture, for the most part reused and of various provenance, must have been concentrated in the *natatio*, the *frigidarium*, the gymnasia (*palaestrae*),

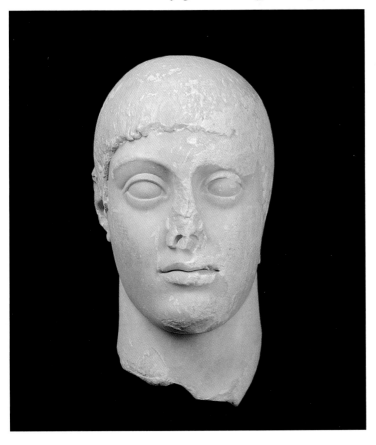

6. *Head of a young athlete from the Baths of Diocletian (from the* natatio *area, later occupied by the Ludovisi Cloister). Hadrianic-period copy of an original Greek bronze from the early fifth century BC*

7. Statue of the Aphrodite of Cnidos from the Baths of Diocletian (external rectangular exedra of the northwestern wing of the Basilica of Santa Maria degli Angeli e dei Martiri). Copy from the early Imperial era inspired by Praxiteles' celebrated Greek original

8. Male torso from the Baths of Diocletian (external rectangular exedra of the Basilica of Santa Maria degli Angeli e dei Martiri, together with the Aphrodite of Cnidos). Copy from the early Imperial era of a Greek original of the Classical period

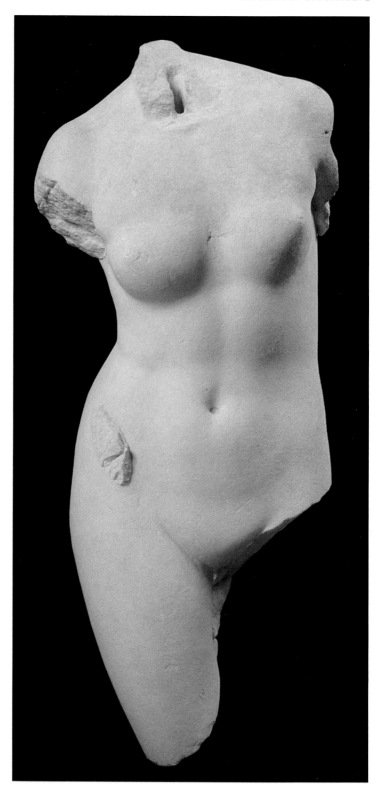

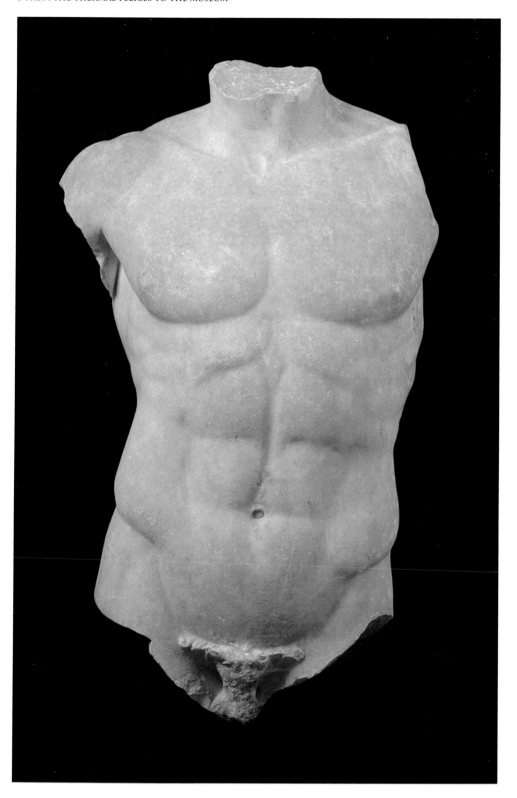

The Philosophers of the Baths

The sculptor and architect Flaminio Vacca (1538-1605) left a precious account of the excavations in Rome during the sixteenth century in his *Memorie di varie antichità trovate in diversi luoghi della città di Roma*, written in 1594, though not published until 1704. Although the book suffers from a style which strains to amaze the reader, and therefore favors anecdotes over hard facts, the information it contains is often of great value. Vacca describes a mid-century discovery in the area of the Baths, probably during the pontificate of Pius IV (1559–65) in the following terms (*Mem*: 104):

"The owner of a vineyard behind the Baths of Diocletian, wanting to install a shed for storing the cultivating tools, discovered two walls jutting out of the ground, and starting to dig between them, and seeing that the ground gave way, saw a hole, enlarged it, and entered.

[The room] was shaped like an oven, and in it he found eighteen philosophers' heads on the ground, which he sold for 700 *scudi* to sig. Gio. Giorgio Cesarini, and now the sig. Giuliano has sold them to cardinal Farnese, and they are in his gallery."

A series of fourteen heads of philosophers in the Museo Archeologico Nazionale in Naples have recently been identified as belonging to this group of statues from the Farnese collection.

9. Bust of Posidonius of Apamea. Augustan period. Naples, Museo Archeologico Nazionale

10. Herm of Zeno. Copy from the early Imperial era of an original from the beginning of the Hellenistic period. Naples, Museo Archeologico Nazionale

and the adjoining rooms. The evidence from the source-sites of the few statues recovered from within the main block also supports this hypothesis: a male torso, a statue of the Aphrodite of Cnidos, and a head of an athlete—works datable to the beginning of the Imperial Era and to the Hadrianic period, and therefore recycled.

There were probably other statues arranged in the gardens, as was usual in the late-Imperial bath complexes; this, at least, is suggested by a headless herm representing the poet Ennius, which perhaps belonged to a gallery of portraits of poets. This was likely counterbalanced by a gallery of philosophers, whose vestiges are recognized in the eighteen heads of philosophers in the Farnese collection, fourteen of which have been recently identified upon comparison with a series of portraits in the Museo Archeologico in Naples. We do not know much about the original placement of a headless statue of a male wearing a toga, datable to the third century AD, but its finding seems to attest to the presence of honorary and "iconic" statues within the bath complex.

A number of authors from the fifteenth century onwards have left records of the discoveries of other statues in the area of the Baths. In general, the information is frustratingly vague, and does not allow a secure identification with any of the pieces in foreign or Italian museums or collections. But we do know, for example, that the Baths yielded the huge monolithic red porphyry basin (some four meters in diameter and thirteen in circumference) which decorates the center of the *Sala Rotonda* of the Vatican Museums. Another four basins from the Baths are also conserved: one, in pink granite, in the very same Vatican Museums; another, in green porphyry, in the *Museo Nazionale Romano*; and two, in gray granite, in the *Staatliche Museen* in Berlin.

The water supply was provided by a branch—or, more precisely, the final segment—of the *Aqua Marcia*, called the *Aqua Iovia* or *Iobia* after a title the Emperor added in AD 286 (the name was later extended to all of the aqueduct and its branches). Once inside the *Porta Tiburtina*, carried above ground on a series of arches, it emptied into a vast trapezoidal *piscina* (32) situated outside the complex walls along the southeastern side, not far from the *Porta Viminalis*. This enormous cistern, known as the *Botte di Termini*, or "Barrel of Termini," was about 91 meters long, with a median width of 16 meters, and was subdivided by pilasters into several naves (from two to five). Later on, however, the water supply was assured by reservoirs located within the interior of the complex, as is evidenced in the transformation of Room XI of the *Museo Nazionale Romano* (20b), which shows traces of a waterproof coating on both the floor and the walls.

On the basis of what we know, it is possible to assert that, in the Baths of Diocletian, architecture, decoration, and technical skill combined to

The Aqua Marcia

The Baths of Diocletian were supplied with water from the *Aqua Marcia*, built by the praetor Q. *Marcius Rex* in 144 BC, and already restored a number of times before Diocletian's reign, starting with Agrippa in 33 BC.

The aqueduct's source was a series of springs in the upper Aniene valley, near mile XXXVI of the *Via Valeria*, perhaps including the *Rosoline* and the *Seconda Serena* near present-day Marano Equo.

The aqueduct followed the course of the Aniene until Tivoli, then circled around south toward the *Via Prenestina*, running alongside the *Via Latina* for a stretch, to then enter the city at the Porta Maggiore (*ad Spem Veterem*), skirt north by the *Porta Tiburtina*, and empty into the enormous *Botte di Termini*, in the area of the *Porta Viminalis*. From this main reservoir, a number of branches supplied water to ten of the city's fourteen *regiones*. The total length of the

aqueduct, from its sources to Rome, was 61,710 paces, or 91.33 km. 80 km of this ran underground, and the rest on arches and substructures.

The water was quite cold, of excellent quality, and very abundant: Frontinus (*Dell'acquedotto della città di Roma*, 67, 68) gives its volume as 4690 *quinarie*, equal to 188,000 cubic meters per day, and in its modern reconstruction it remains one of the most important sources of water for Rome.

produce a harmonious and functional whole, thoroughly justifying the expression *omni cultu perfectas* in the dedication which underlines the precise intention of its illustrious patron concerning the *thermas felices Diocletianas*. For the rest, the appreciation of the ancient authors for the Baths is well illustrated by the excerpt from Juvenal (11. 50. 1), in which he praises the *solitudo* of this spot, which was a veritable oasis of tranquility in the chaotic daily world of late-Imperial Rome.

The Baths of Diocletian have been severely damaged and abused through the centuries; its buildings, subjected to innumerable transformations, have been converted to the widest possible variety of uses. In the following pages, we will retrace a rough outline of the most important steps in a still-ongoing evolution.

An inscription copied by Fra Giocondo of Verona around 1495 (*CIL* VI, 1131: *Thermas Diocletianas a veteribus principib(us) institutas omn[- - -]*) appears to record a first attempt at restoration, most likely in response to the damages the city suffered during the sack by Alaric's Visigoths in AD 410. Archeological evidence tends to confirm this reading, in particular an Ionic capital and other architectonic fragments found in the Baths which are datable to the end of the fourth or beginning of the fifth century.

During the course of the fifth century, the church of San Ciriaco in Thermis was built in honor of the deacon and martyr within the northern corner of the outer wall. (The first mention of the *titulus Sancti Cyriaci* dates from AD 499; the church was active until the sixteenth century.) According to a legend which blossomed during the Middle Ages, Cyriac owned a house near the Baths, and distinguished himself by providing succor to those thousands of Christians (up to 40,000 according to some sources!) whom Diocletian had impiously condemned to work on the Baths—work during the course of which many of them died from the forced labor and unspeakable hardships. Still in function at the time of Sidonius Apollinare (*Carmi*, 23, AD 495–99) and during the first decades of the sixth century, the Baths suffered serious damage, along with the rest of the city, during the Gothic Wars (535–53). The disruption of the aqueducts by Vitige's Ostrogoths in 537, together with the subsequent devastations inflicted by those of Totila in 546, resulted in the abandonment of the *thermae*. From that moment on, the Baths (located in the fourth ecclesiastical region: *Reg. Honor.* I, AD 625) were transformed, as is the case with most other monuments of Imperial Rome, into a vast quarry providing materials (marble, travertine, etc.) for reuse in new constructions. The local inhabitants also excavated galleries underneath the building to retrieve the prized *pozzolana* of the Viminal Hill; this eventually destabilized the substructure and caused vaults to cave in. A part of the area was also occasionally used for a burial ground. Fires and earthquakes did the rest.

The memory of the *thermae*, however, remained alive throughout the Medieval Era; in fact, the Baths of Diocletian are systematically cited in the various editions of the *Mirabilia Urbis* (*Mirabilia Urbis,* 5 *Graphia aureae Urbis,* 16; *Le miracle de Rome,* 24; *De Mirabilibus Civitatis Romae,* 9), a sign that they constituted a must-see for the *romei* or pilgrims, during their stay in the city. One of the many visitors, between the end of the twelfth century and the beginning of the thirteenth century, was a certain Magister Gregory, an English theologian with a passion for antiquity who wrote one of the most famous and eccentric editions of the *Mirabilia* (*Narracio de mirabilius Urbis Romae*)

11. *Antonio da Sangallo the Elder (1455–1534). Elevation of the Baths of Diocletian. Florence, Uffizi Gallery, Gabinetto dei Disegni e delle Stampe*

12. *Baldassarre Peruzzi (1481–1526). Section of the Baths of Diocletian. Florence, Uffizi Gallery, Gabinetto dei Disegni e delle Stampe*

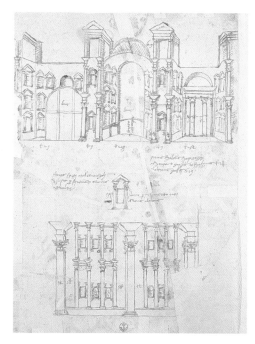

The Anonymous Destailleur Architectural Codex

The codex gets its name from its last private owner, the French architect Hyppolite Destailleur, a collector of drawings who sold part of his collection in 1879 to the Kunstbibliothek (at that time the Kunstgewerbemuseum) in Berlin, where it is still conserved today.
It is not actually a true codex, but rather a collection of 120 sheets of various formats, with mid-sixteenth-century drawings on both sides showing important buildings of ancient and Renaissance Rome. The sheets bear annotations in two or three hands, both in French and in a shaky Italian, including a great number of measurements, and seem to be the result of a veritable survey undertaken by one or more anonymous French-speaking artists in Rome, probably in the entourage of cardinal Jean du Bellay.
The artist, whose interest is almost exclusively architectonic, treats the Baths of Diocletian with a characteristic accuracy and attention to detail in thirteen of the drawings (40-52), reproducing various parts of the complex in plan, section, and elevation. These are of particular interest in that the survey precedes Michelangelo's transformation of the main central halls into the church of Santa Maria degli Angeli. The two drawings reproduced here are among the most significant: a cross section along the central axis of the bath building, showing, from left to right, the *caldarium-tepidarium-frigidarium-natatio* axis (which reproduces the heating system of the *caldarium*); and a drawing of the *natatio*'s façade, with its structure intact but already missing the statues in the niches.

13. Anonymous French artist. Reconstruction of the façade of the natatio *of the Baths of Diocletian. Berlin, Kunstbibliothek, Destailleur Codex B*

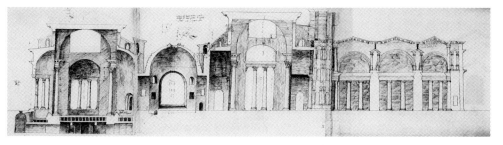

Petrarch himself, in a famous letter (*Epist. famil.* 6, 2), expresses a lively fascination for the Baths, where he often went during his stay in Rome in order to contemplate the imposing ruins, and evoke the grandeur of ancient Rome.

The Baths conserved a good part of their marble decoration through the Renaissance. Giovanni Rucellai's description of the condition of the building in the mid-fifteenth century sounds reliable, and we have an ample graphic archive from various artists of the late fifteenth, and, especially, the sixteenth century—drawings and prints of plans, sections, reconstructions, and *vedute*—by artists and architects including Bramante, Antonio and Giuliano da Sangallo, Sansovino, Baldassarre Peruzzi, Andrea Palladio, Hieronymus Cock, Hendrick van Cleef, Antonio Dosio, and Étienne Du Pérac, as well as the anonymous artists who produced the drawings of the Destailleur Codex, and the artists from the school of Raphael who also left a number of drawings.

This atmosphere of renewed interest in the building produced the first significant recoveries of sculpture from the complex, as evidenced, for example, in the haphazard dig described by Flaminio Vacca.

In the meantime, during the first decades of the sixteenth century, the *frigidarium* (10) had been outfitted as an equitation hall for the use of young Roman aristocrats, and public jousting matches were held in it, such as the one in 1536 in which several English knights participated. Private homes, storehouses, and barns had as well taken over a number of structures of the bath complex, and gardens and vineyards were planted in the environs.

Around the middle of the century (or shortly before—we have records of his definitive residence by 1548), the French cardinal and diplomat Jean du Bellay came into possession of an estate which included the surviving structures on the southwest side of the outer wall of the Baths (the large exedra and the spaces surrounding it, including the two rotundas). A prominent personality in the French court of Francis I, cultured and refined (his private doctor, François Rabelais, the celebrated author of *Gargantua and Pantagruel*, followed him to Rome), with a passion for antiquity and for collecting antiquities, du Bellay converted a part of the estate between 1554 and 1555 into a picturesque *viridarium*, or archeological garden, known as the *Horti Belleiani* (or *Bellaiani*), decorated with two series of ancient statues, one in the *casino*, and the other lining the paths of the garden.

After du Bellay's death in 1560, his heirs sold the property to pay off the estate's debts. Cardinal Carlo Borromeo acquired it for 8000 Roman *scudi*, and then passed it on to his uncle, Pope Pius IV, for the same amount.

Pius IV is responsible for the most important of the transformations regarding the complex, undertaken at the urging of a Sicilian priest,

14. Anonymous French artist. Longitudinal section of the Baths of Diocletian with pertinent details. Berlin, Kunstbibliothek, Destailleur Codex B

15. Antonio da Sangallo the Elder (1455–1534). Plan of the Baths of Diocletian. Florence, Uffizi Gallery, Gabinetto dei Disegni e delle Stampe

16. Hieronymus Cock (1510–1570). Elevation of the Baths of Diocletian. Rome, Istituto Nazionale per la Grafica, Gabinetto delle Stampe

17. Hendrick van Cleef (1524–1589). The Baths of Diocletian. Rome, Istituto Nazionale per la Grafica, Gabinetto delle Stampe

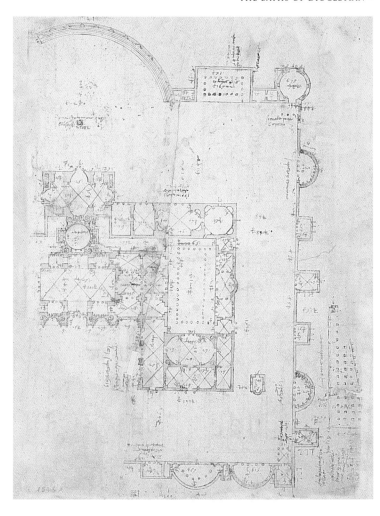

the visionary Antonio del Duca of Cefalù. A papal bull of July 27, 1561, ordered the construction of a church in the *frigidarium* area, consecrated to the cult of the Madonna of the Angels and to the memory of the Christian martyrs who, according to tradition, had been put to work as the construction crew of the Baths. The direction of the church was conceded to the Carthusian monks of Santa Croce in Gerusalemme, who were installed in a monastery built next door.

The idea of founding a church inside the Baths was not a new one. A similar project had already been proposed at the end of the eleventh century by Pope Urban II, who towards this end conceded the area in 1091 to the future Saints Bruno and Gavino, and, in the mid-fourteenth century, by Napoleone and Nicolò Orsini. The realization of these projects, however, fell to Pius IV.

He gave the job of transforming the building to the by-then elderly Michelangelo. Construction work started in 1562, and continued into the late 1580s. Michelangelo's project largely respected the original architecture of the edifice; essentially, he limited himself to uniting the *frigidarium* with the two adjoining rooms at each end, creating a Greek

EX RVINIS THERMARVM IMP. DIOCLITIANI, PROSPECTVS VNVS,

5. Henri. Cliuen. inuen   Thermæ Diocletiani.   Philipp. Gall. excud

Vestigii delle Terme di Diocletiano, dalla parte di dentro che guarda uerso sirocco, nelle quali si puol conprendere la smisurata altezza, et larghezza delle uolte, la magnificenza è grandezza di dicto castino. Nella parte segnata A, era un Atrio ouero Cortile con colonne attorno quale sostenuano un coritore p poteru passegiare sotto al coperto, il pauimento era di diuerse pietre mischie, che faceuano bellis= conpartimenti lauorati di musaice. Nella parte segnata B, si uede la Pinacotheca, ouero luogo doue erano usati trattenimenti di pitture, sculture e adornata di grandis= sollonne di granito un h lor proprii.
Marco Sadeler excudit

18. Girolamo Ferri
(active in the mid-
seventeenth century).
Ruins of the Baths of
Diocletian. Rome,
Istituto Nazionale
per la Grafica, Gabinetto
delle Stampe

Cross plan which emphasized the transversal nave, the *crociera*. Regular services were held as early as 1565 in the church, to which Pius IV transferred the cardinalate of the nearby San Ciriaco.

At the same time, the Carthusians built the large adjacent monastery at their own expense, following a design by Giacomo del Duca; he installed a small cloister to the right of the church's presbytery, in the area of the *natatio*, and built a large cloister (following a project presumably by Giacomo del Duca begun in 1565) between the central bath building and the northern corner of the outer wall. The monks' cells were distributed along the northwest, and part of the southwest, sides of this larger cloister.

In 1575, Gregory XIII, looking to provide a dignified seat for Rome's grain distribution agency (the *Annona frumentaria*), transformed the halls on the west side of the *caldarium* (13a-16a) into storehouses, known as the *horrea Ecclesiae*. These were subsequently enlarged several times: once by Paul V, who in 1609 incorporated the hall of Sant'Isidoro in Thermis and its adjacent rooms (17a-20a), as well as the octagonal hall, which may have already been a part of Gregory XIII's granary; again by Urban VIII, who in 1640 extended the building in a direction perpendicular to the Pauline granary as far as Via Pia (the present-day Via XX Settembre); and, finally, by Clement XI, who added the *Granari Nuovi* in 1705 on the southwest side of the outer wall, at the corner of the former Via degli Strozzi, and restored the rotunda in the corner of the outer wall (7b).

The ancient structures of the bath complex suffered severe damage following the reconversion of the area by pope Sixtus V. Beginning in 1576, well before his ascent to the papal throne, he began acquiring the land around Termini Station (the name is an obvious deformation of the Latin *thermae*, which had in time come to indicate the neighborhood in the environs of the Baths themselves), and commissioned his architect, Domenico Fontana, to lay out what was at the time the largest villa in Rome: villa Montalto Peretti, model for the subsequent great baroque villas of the city.

The villa's construction led to the demolition of a good number of the Baths' remaining structures (Fontana, in his *Libri dei Conti*, refers to them colorfully as "the hulks of *Termine*," and "junk"). In addition, the southern corner of the outer wall was razed to clear the land for a new street from Termini to Porta Tiburtina. Part of the enormous quantity of masonry recovered was used as landfill to level the streetpath and the villa's terrain. A large strip of the remaining southeast outer wall was exploited in 1585–88 to install the Palazzo di Termini, with stables and barns, and the *botteghe di Farfa*. The latter were eighteen shops with sleeping spaces, built to house the merchants of the famous market fair (*Fiera*) of Farfa, which took place every September in the Sabine city of the same name, and which the Pope wanted to transfer to his villa in order to develop the commercial activity in the area. The project to move the fair fell through, and the space was rented out for several years to silkworkers. The *Botte di Termini* cistern was incorporated into the villa complex, and the *Aqua Iovia* restored and connected to the new conduit of the *Acqua Felice*.

In 1593, Caterina Nobili Sforza, niece of Pope Julius III and widow of the Sforza Count of Santa Fiora, bought the *Horti Belleiani* from the Carthusians for 10,000 Roman *scudi*—her family had been renting them since 1579—and the next year donated them to the reformed Cistercian congregation of the *Folianti*. Between 1594 and 1596, she had the *casino* of the *Horti Belleiani* (in the center of the large exedra of the Baths, at the opening of the present Via Nazionale) restructured into the church of Santa Caterina in Thermis, which was abandoned in 1817 and demolished in 1870. Several years later, in 1598, the same donna Caterina undertook, at her own expense, the transformation of the rotunda (7a) in the southwest corner of the outer precinct wall into a church. Completed in 1600, it was dedicated two years later to Saint Bernard of Clair-

19. The gardens of Villa Montalto and the Casino Felice in the second half of the seventeenth century

FONTANA NEL GIARDINO MONTALTO
su l monte Viminale uerso Santa Maria maggiore. Architettura del Caualier Domenico Fontana
Gio Francesco Venturini del. et inc.   G.Iac.Rossi le stampa in Roma alla pace con Priu.del S.Pont.

16

*20. View of the cloister
of Michelangelo
(or the large cloister)
before its restoration*

vaux, and goes by the name of San Bernardo alle Terme. During the course of the seventeenth century, in addition to the previously mentioned interventions, there were also further discoveries of statues and fragments of the architectonic decoration of the complex, and the activity of the *pozzolana* quarriers continued unabated.

The eighteenth century saw other important readaptations and transformations of the ancient bath buildings. In 1749, Cardinal Bichi, a patron of the Carthusians, decided to enlarge the basilica of Santa Maria degli Angeli, and gave the commission to Luigi Vanvitelli, who elaborated a project with the aim of clearing the Michelangelesque structure of the numerous later (and heavy-handed) interventions, while at the same time giving the longitudinal nave the same importance as that of the transversal axis.

In 1754, Benedict XIV restored the granaries of the *Annona*, and built a chapel to Saint Isidoro (Sant'Isidoro in Thermis) within the Pauline granary, in the bath building adjacent to the octagonal hall. Clement XIII, in 1764, added storehouses to the Gregorian granary to stock the city's oil-rations (the *Olearie*). 1772 saw the installation within the ruins of the Baths of the *Fabbrica della Calancà*, an atelier specialized in the printing of cotton fabrics of the "calancà" type, in tandem with a program of cotton cultivation in the Pontine marshes. The military guard posted by the Popes to defend the *cittadella annonaria* occupied another sector of the bath complex.

At the time of the French occupation (1809–14), the Carthusian monastery was converted into a barracks, and the spaces surrounding the basilica of Santa Maria degli Angeli were sold to private concerns and converted into storehouses. Pius VII, having ended the grain and oil hand-outs of the *Annona*, decided to found the *Pio Istituto Generale di Carità* in 1816 as a shelter for beggars, and set it up in the former granaries. The *Pio Istituto* later became the *Pia Casa d'Industria e Lavoro*, and, later still, the Santa Maria degli Angeli Hospice for the Poor. Throughout the length of the nineteenth century, sheds, taverns, woodsheds, coal-holes, warehouses and laundries continued to attach themselves a bit everywhere to the ancient and more recent structures in the zone.

The *pensionnaires* in architecture at the French Academy in Rome have left a precious graphic archive (surveys and reconstructions) of the area of the Baths during this period in the *envois* which they regularly sent to Paris. A. Famin, Ch.-H. Landon, Fl. Boulanger, E. Brune, and Ed.-J.-B. Paulin were among the architects who took a special interest in the Baths during the last century.

The proclamation of Rome as capital of Italy in 1861, and, ten years later, the transferral of the capital of the Kingdom from Florence to Rome, opened a phase of profound urban transformation in the city (and in this area in particular) which had important consequences for the remains of the ancient bath complex.

Following the construction of the first papal railroad line (Rome–Frascati, inaugurated on July 7, 1856), the "Farfa bottegas" were reconverted in 1861 to house the first, provisional, Central Train Station, which opened at the end of 1862. At this time the *Botte di Termini* cistern was razed to the level of the track foundations; it had already been partially demolished in 1742 by the heirs of Cardinal Giovan Francesco Negroni, who succeeded the Peretti Montalto family as owner of Sixtus V's sumptuous villa.

The subsequent construction work for the new Central Station, which began in 1874 and involved the creation of a new surrounding neighborhood, provoked enormous damage to the ancient monument. Between 1874 and 1875, the empty "Farfa bottegas" were demolished; the large exedra on the southeast side of the outer wall which had been integrated into the shops, and whose ancient structure still reached a height of some five meters, was at first spared, and then, in 1878, also destroyed. In 1875, the northeast stretch of the *Botte di Termini* was completely demolished.

In the meantime, with the abolition of the ecclesiastical orders (extended to Rome in 1873), the congregations of the Cistercians of San Bernardo and of the Carthusians of Santa Maria degli Angeli were dissolved; the last Carthusians left in 1884. Those spaces not in private

21. Ed.-J.-B. Paulin, Elevation and longitudinal section of the Baths of Diocletian, 1880

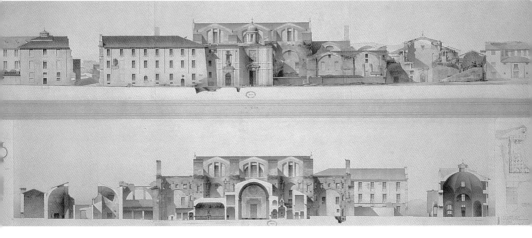

hands met with a variety of ends; the "Margherita di Savoia" hospice for the blind, the *Scuola Normale* for Girls, and a barracks were among the institutions housed in the ruins.

In the following years, the *thermae* suffered further serious damage due to an urban renewal program involving the construction of a number of large buildings in the zone—including the Grand Hotel, the Ministry of Finances, and the Palazzo Massimo—and the realization of Piazza dell'Esedra, whose plan, by G. Koch, retraced the outline of the Baths' ancient monumental exedra on a slightly smaller scale. This phase of construction also led to the opening in 1878 of Via Cernaia, which cut the central block of the Baths in two; to the demolition of the remaining traces of the *caldarium*, and of a portion of the great exedra (1887); and, in the same year, to the destruction of parts of the outer wall along Via XX Settembre and near the train station.

In 1889, the decision to house a museum within the bath-monastery complex opened a new chapter in the history of the building's transformations, and at the same time initiated a process which aimed to recuperate the ancient structures, and thereby permit a reevaluation of their true worth. These decisions crowned a series of attempts undertaken in the preceding years to endow the new capital of the Kingdom of Italy with a national museum of antiquities capable of holding its own beside the collections of the Vatican and Capitoline Museums.

With Royal Decree no. 5958 of February 7, 1889, the Minister of Public Instruction, Paolo Boselli, instituted a National Museum in Rome, following the initiative of Felice Barnabei, divided into two sections: the first consisting of finds from within the city of Rome, to be housed in the Baths of Diocletian (the future *Museo Nazionale Romano*); the second comprising antiquities from outside Rome, to be housed in the Villa Giulia (the future *Museo Nazionale Etrusco*). This museum was inaugurated on June 1, 1890; the section destined for the Baths was initially set up in several of the Carthusian cells, in the large cloister, and in the gardens giving onto the Piazza dei Cinquecento.

The following years saw the elaboration of several projects "to redeem the Baths of Diocletian," motivated by the immediately perceived need to endow the new museum with new exhibition spaces, and the equally urgent need to free the ancient monument from the innumerous additions and alterations suffered throughout its history as a result of its improper use. An important archeological exhibition organized in Rome in 1911 to celebrate the fiftieth anniversary of the proclamation of Italian unity gave an opportunity to put these projects into execution. Law no. 502, passed on July 11, 1907, set aside the necessary funds to expropriate the private buildings which encrusted the Baths, and to proceed with the restoration and renovation of the bath complex.

However, opposition by the owners and renters of the private buildings slowed down the start of the work, which in fact proceeded only when a prefectural decree of December 14, 1909 ordered the immediate occupation of the properties on the site. The construction, financed partly by the Ministry of Public Instruction, and partly by the Committee in charge of the festivities for 1911, caused the demolition of a good number of these structures, which in the course of time had finished by hiding the ancient walls. Remains of the *natatio* were brought to light, and workers restored the seven halls arranged next to the right wing of the transept of Santa Maria degli Angeli, which had been converted into a complex including a tavern, warehouses, bakery, and stables (26b, 28b-31b), and the two easternmost rooms of the *frigida-*

rium, furnished with basins. The remains of the halls looking onto Via Cernaia were recovered (17a-20a), some of which had been converted into stables for the city cleaning crew, as well as the octagonal hall (16a). Also, Luigi Vanvitelli's eighteenth-century façade on Santa Maria degli Angeli was demolished in order to reveal one of the two larger apses of the *caldarium* (12).

The 1911 Archeological Exhibition was set up in the seven halls next to the right wing of the transept of Santa Maria degli Angeli, and those which flanked the *natatio* on its eastern side (20b-23b); these rooms afterward formed the nucleus of the *Museo Nazionale Romano*.

The 1930s brought another campaign to isolate and restore the ancient bath buildings, which involved the demolition of Paul V's and Urban VIII's granaries, among other structures. During this period the transformation of the Baths' halls into a museum space was fully realized.

None of the subsequent interventions to restore and/or maintain the bath complex have significantly altered the structure of the edifice. On the other hand, the work is still continuing on the project to recover and functionally present the spaces of archeological and historical interest, undertaken especially in the octagonal hall and the adjacent hall of Sant'Isidoro (discussed in greater detail below), but also involving other spaces such as the *Olearie*, and the so-called hall of Monteporzio (once the seat of the *Associazione dei Garibaldini*). [GT]

22. The Michelangelesque Cloister after restoration seen from a different angle

The 1911 Archeological Exhibition

In 1911, for the fiftieth anniversary of Italian unity, the government organized a fitting program of festivities, including commemorative ceremonies, exhibitions, and other spectacles, in the three cities which had been capitals of the Kingdom of Italy: Turin, Florence and Rome. In Rome, the projects included an archeological exhibition to be set up in the Baths of Diocletian, restored for that purpose. Rodolfo Lanciani was named curator of the exhibition, and Giulio Quirino Giglioli was made the general secretary.

The preparatory work for the show began in 1908, although the recuperation and renovation of the exhibition spaces did not get underway until the end of 1909.

The Archeological Exhibition was officially inaugurated on April 8, 1911, in the presence of the royal couple, Vittorio Emanuele III and Elena of Montenegro, and their guests, who included Imperial German princes.

The exhibition was organized in 21 sections, and set up in the restored bath halls, the smaller cloister of the Carthusian monastery, the octagonal hall, and the Baths' gardens, and was composed almost exclusively of plaster casts and reproductions, scale models, drawings, and photographs—some commissioned by the organizers of the exhibition and involving expensive expeditions, such as the one carried out by Azeglio Berretti

to document the temple of Rome and Augustus in Ankara (the ancient Ancyra), and some sent by nations which were formerly Roman provinces. A few original pieces completed the show. The first three sections of the exhibition ("Eternal Rome," "The Roman *Imperium*," and "The Divine Augustus," respectively) provide an introduction of sorts to that universe of ideals and values which defined *Romanità*, or "Roman-ness," consciously propagated throughout a large swath of the ancient world, partly for purposes of Imperial propaganda, and partly out of the City's sincere sense of a mission to civilize at least its part of the world. The following sections display pieces relevant to the various provinces of the Empire, furnishing a concrete sense of this cultural adherence, and allowing an informed evaluation of the impact Roman civilization had on these territories.

Sections 9 ("Laurentum") and 10 ("Monuments in Crete") were intended to give a sampling of the most recent discoveries by Italian archeologists; the "Gallery of Treasures," section 12, housed reproductions of ancient jewelry.

The exhibition concluded with two sections devoted to particularly significant sites: "Ara Pacis-Pydna-Platorini" (section 20) and "Ancyra" (section 21), and in the octagonal hall there was a corollary display of a large scale map (1:400) of the center of fourth century Imperial Rome by the French architect Bigot.

But in order to give an understanding of the intentions behind the exhibition, it is best to quote directly from the speech given by Rodolfo Lanciani at the inauguration: "Our objectives are threefold. First, we have tried, above all, to create a picture of Roman civilization under the Empire, asking all of her 36 provinces for some record of the benefits conferred by Rome upon the various aspects of public and private life, and especially in the realm of public works. Then we started to try to give her back—at least in the form of copies—the artistic treasures she has lost since the Renaissance to foreign museums. Third, we attempted to reconstitute various monuments and statuary groups which had been plundered and dispersed through the centuries."

On the whole, the 1911 Archeological Exhibition represented a large-scale international cultural campaign, and constituted, fifty years after the proclamation of Italian unity, a first serious attempt at reflection upon the national identity and the common origins of the Italian people in the context of historical and archeological research. Certainly, the exhibition's emphasis on the role and civilizing effect of Rome in the ancient world finished, inevitably, by assuming a propagandistic edge, given the hopes and expectations of redemption of a still young nation, and its renewed colonial aspirations—in 1911, after all, Giolitti's

"Italietta" started the Libyan War.

But such tendencies, far from being specific to Italy, were in fact typical of the predominant historiographical orientation of the age, and do not take away from the exhibition's many important merits: its rigorous and serious scientific preparation; the sheer abundance of the material; the possibility of reconstituting monuments and sculptural groups long broken up and whose pieces were scattered in various museums around the world, using either original fragments or copies (these included the tomb of the Platorini and the Altar of Domitian Enobarbus, the latter assembling casts of the reliefs now in the Louvre and the Glyptothek of Munich); or, still yet, the thorough documentary overview of the most significant results of modern Italian archeological studies. The exhibition, in short, exhorted the viewer to confront and resolve the problems of archeological research in scientific terms. These motives guaranteed a lasting impact from the experience of the 1911 exhibition.

As Lanciani himself said: "We say all of this to demonstrate that the Committee, in organizing the exhibition, had a clear and determined concept—refraining from spending the money in ephemeral ways, and choosing instead to assemble a valuable collection of material which would retain a permanent documentary value."

Lanciani had to wait a number of years before his wishes found concrete form; it was not until 1926 that the Governor of Rome took up the challenge and instituted a Museum of the Roman Empire in Rome with the material from the 1911 exhibition. The new museum was inaugurated on April 21, 1927, in a wing of the former convent of Sant'Ambrogio, in the ghetto near Piazza Mattei. By May 24, 1929, the collection, enriched and reorganized, had been transferred to the Palazzo dei Musei (formerly the Pantanella pasta factory) in Piazza Bocca della Verità. The museum's exhibits formed part of the *Mostra Augustea della Romanità*, opened on September 23, 1937, in the Palazzo delle Esposizioni on Via Nazionale, and finished by constituting the nucleus of the Museo della Civiltà Romana at E.U.R., partially inaugurated in May 1952, and fully opened to the public on April 21, 1955.

23. Plan of the 1911 Archeological Exhibition

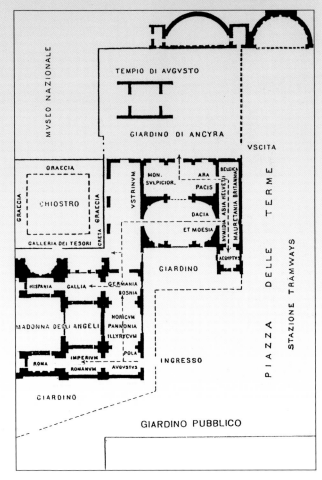

MUSEO NAZIONALE ROMANO
THE BATHS OF DIOCLETIAN

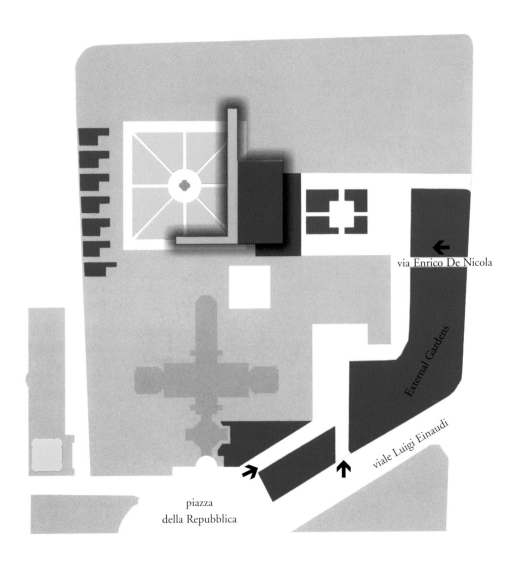

via Enrico De Nicola

External Gardens

viale Luigi Einaudi

piazza
della Repubblica

The External Gardens
The Garden of the Five Hundred

The Epigraphic Section

Protohistory of the Latin Peoples

The Michelangelesque Cloister

Octagonal Hall (Planetarium)

THE COLLECTIONS OF THE
MUSEO NAZIONALE ROMANO

After thorough scientific studies, research into the archives and deposits and well-thought-out restoration campaigns, the extraordinary archeological patrimony of the Museo Nazionale Romano has finally found an adequate presentation, informed by refined exhibition schemes, in various seats: Palazzo Massimo, Palazzo Altemps, Crypta Balbi. While the large halls of the Baths of Diocletian have been used for important temporary exhibitions, the suggestive space of the *Rotonda* (ex-Planetarium) houses a permanent collection of sculpture found in Bath complexes, and the adjacent hall of Sant'Isidoro displays the material recovered in Trastevere during the excavation of a sanctuary to Hercules. The historic seat of the Museo Nazionale Romano next to the Baths now houses the vast epigraphic collection, the open walkways of the ground floor of the Michelangelesque cloister of the old Carthusian monastery is adorned with statues, and the closed attic corridors surrounding the cloister develop an interesting itinerary exploring the proto-history of the Latin peoples. The Baths of Diocletian are easily one of the best conserved archeological areas of Rome, freely appreciated by visiting the structures visible in the garden or the underground excavations visible in the floor of the Octagonal Hall.

*26. External view
of the exhibition halls
on the eastern side
of the Baths, to the side
of the present entrance
to the museum*

*27. External views
of the halls next
to the* frigidarium

*28. External view, from
Via Luigi Einaudi,
of the halls located
between the* frigidarium
and the southeast
palaestra

The External Gardens

There are three entrances to the museum: one in Piazza della Repubblica, just beyond the entrance to the church of Santa Maria degli Angeli in the direction of Termini Station; the second on Via Luigi Einaudi; and the third in front of Termini Station, at Via Enrico De Nicola number 78. The outer gardens are communal property, but have for some years now been placed under the jurisdiction of the Archeological Superintendence, and the museum takes responsibility for their landscaping and maintenance. The pathways and flowerbeds have been arranged with large-scale architectural elements and a number of undecorated or scarcely decorated sarcophagi in order to create, for the visitor who comes in from the chaos and degradation of the surrounding areas, a sort of gradual introduction into the exhibition halls properly speaking (figs. 26, 27). The walkway entering from Via De Nicola is introduced on either side by two sarcophagi with minimal decorations of architectural motifs, characteristic of the early productions of the workshops in the urban area of Rome and datable to the first half of the first century AD. One of the more interesting pieces is the large sarcophagus in travertine placed in the walkway at the angle of Via De Nicola and Via Einaudi, which imitates the production of the island of Proconnesus in the typical form of its chest and its double-sloped *lid*, as well as in the decorative motif of the platter with handles. It comes from a sepulchral chamber out the Via Nomentana near Mentana, and can be dated to the second half of the second century AD. Another interesting example, to the right of the walkway entering from Via Einaudi, presents surfaces roughly blocked out and ready to receive a sculpted decoration which remained undone. In front of this last piece, against the walls of the museum, a large vase (*dolus*) (fig. 28) atop a column bears an inscription recording the work of the architect G. Koch for the realization between 1896 and 1902 of Piazza dell'Esedra, which retraces the internal wall of the large exedra of the Baths. At the end of this pathway, before the staircase leading into the large halls, stands the statue of the Samnite warrior placed here on the occasion of the exhibition "The Italy of the Samnites" in 1999. A work of the sculptor G. Guastalla from 1922, and originally intended for the center of Pietrabbondate, it is noteworthy for the care and philological precision in the treatment of all the attributes and details of the armor.

The Garden of the Five Hundred

From the external garden on the side of Via De Nicola, one enters into a second green space which has been an integral part of the museum since its inception. The use of this space as gardens is already documented in nineteenth century maps and inscriptions. The recent thorough restoration retained the general layout of the beds as set in a project of the 1950s, while reordering the archeological material, which had grown too crowded in the last two decades.

Just inside the gate (fig. 29), on both sides and atop the short walls delimiting the beds of grass, is arranged a series of funerary altars, both of a votive nature and of the type containing the ashes of the deceased, and with inscriptions in both Latin and Greek. Some of these are decorated with typical symbolic motifs of the funerary repertory, such as the eagle, the crown, the *patera*, *bucranium* and garlands. One in particular (immediately to the left on the pathway with the pergola of roses) is noteworthy for the closed door sculpted on its posterior side: a clear allusion to the portal of the Underworld. Most of these are datable to between the end of the Republican period and the first two centuries of the Imperial era, and come from both the city and its suburban vicinity (fig. 30).

Between the first two beds are placed two sarcophagi with chests decorated in strigil, or furrowed, motifs surrounding a central portrait of the deceased. One of these is vaguely defined but unfinished, while the other portrait, on the sarcophagus to the left, has been barely blocked out, as often happened for various reasons including, obviously, the urgency of burial. Both date from the third century AD.

Placed along the central pathway is a series of statues, both masculine and feminine, coming from Rome, its suburban vicinity and indeed all over southern Lazio, almost all of which were originally used in a funerary context. The male figures' togas display variations dating them to various periods from the late Republican period to the late Empire. The

29. General view of the garden toward Piazza dei Cinquecento

30. The pathways of the garden leading toward the great halls

female figures express the preferred typologies of Large and Small Herculaneum-style funerary art, also characterized by rich and ample drapery and by stiff, static poses.

The first two statues at the beginning of the pathway are recognizable as images of two male youths still wearing the *bulla* around their necks. This ornament of Etruscan origin contained an amulet intended to protect the boys until they reached adulthood around the age of seventeen, when they offered it to their Lares. At both their feet lies the *capsa*, a sort of knapsack used to carry scrolls and writing equipment.

At the center of the garden lies the large *crater* in marble decorating the fountain, embellished under the rim with a series of small cupidons. This is a particularly precious example of the monumental vases which were widely used in the ancient world to adorn *atria* in villas, fountains, gardens and open in spaces in general; in Palazzo Massimo, among the paintings from the Villa della Farnesina, one can see a similar vase represented in a garden landscape with the letter L. The calyx was already noted by Gabriele d'Annunzio at the beginning of the twentieth century in his *Halcyon*: "in the courtyard is a large vase amidst verdant greenery. . . the greenery hides the small cupidons sculpted under the lip of the vase." D'Annunzio goes on to describe the garden ("mutilated columns, adorned with worn capitals, urns...") in such a manner as to demonstrate that its aspect has not fundamentally changed in the intervening years (fig. 31). The space surrounding the fountain displays several statues of the aforementioned types and a number of funerary altars, while the pathway along the façade of the museum entrance is lined with various sarcophagi. Some of these are of the most simple and common type, with strigil or furrow motifs, sculpted details in the corners and an epigraph or *imago clipeata* portrait in the center. The decorative motifs are among the most common in funerary art, including figurative representations of the seasons, cupidons with garlands or overturned torches, griffins and horns of plenty. All are datable to the late Imperial era, mostly the third centu-

31. The fountain of the external garden

ry AD, and are mostly from workshops in Rome itself. Of particular interest is the sarcophagus just to the left of the museum entrance, belonging to a freedman of the emperor Antoninus Pius employed in the office of the *annona* (the imperial grain distribution), as the epigraph states.

On the other hand, the sarcophagus with grossly blocked-out garlands in front of the freedman's sarcophagus, which dates from the same period, was imported from Ephesus. It comes from along the Via Salaria at Serpentara, and is an interesting example of how such pieces were put on the market and used even in an unfinished state.

In the pathway which flanks the large exhibition halls of the Baths next to the exit, on the right for those leaving the museum, are displayed a series of memorial stones from tombs indicating the confines and dimensions of the sepulchral areas. These all come from the urban area and are datable to the first two centuries AD. The remaining sculptural material placed on either side of this pathway awaits restoration and final display. A series of *stelae* belonging to various military units line the vehicular road which forms the opposite boundary of the garden. In particular, the first tombstones on the side against the outer wall of the Baths belong to the bodyguard (*corporis custodes*) of the emperor Nero, nicknamed "the Germans," as they were almost all from this ethnic group. These were found along the Via Portuense and date to the years AD 54–68. Another, more conspicuous group follows, belonging to the Praetorian Guard, the imperial guards, and the Urban Cohort dependent on the city prefect. These were unearthed on the right bank of the Tiber near Ponte Milvio, another area of Rome dedicated to military burials. These tombstones are later than the first group and cover a period between the end of the first and the first decades of the second century AD.

The opposite side of this road, flanking the garden, provides a display of simpler tombstones, bearing lists of names and the dimensions of the sepulchral areas to which they belonged. These come for the most part from houses along the consular roads and date from the late Republican era and the first years of the empire.

The Vestibule

Entering from the garden, past the ticket window and bookstore, the visitor comes into the vestibule which opens up into the various museum sections (fig. 32). Given its current aspect in 1911–13, it is a large rectangular space (some 25 meters long by 4.5 meters wide) covered with a barrel vault and divided into three bays by *faux* marble pilasters. In the beginning, when the Carthusian monastery was built, it served as the corridor leading to the Michelangelesque cloister and provided a transitional buffer zone between the spaces of the priory and those strictly pertinent to monastic life. This transitional space has been altered at numerous times during the centuries in function of the various uses of the complex. During the restoration campaign, the walls revealed the presence of interesting fresco paintings representing the Theological Virtues (Faith, Hope and Charity), attributable to Giovanni Odazzi (1663–1731), who also worked in Santa Maria degli Angeli and in San Bernardo alle Terme. For the moment the figure of Charity on the left wall has been partly brought to light; when the restoration will be completed, the other figures should be visible as well, to the extent possible given the superimposed pilaster decoration (fig. 33).

The door in the center of the left wall leads to the small cloister, named the Ludovisi cloister for the collection of ancient sculpture belonging to the Buoncompagni-Ludovisi family which was displayed there at the begin-

32. The vestibule of the museum

33. The fresco of Charity
in the vestibule

ning of the century and is now in the Palazzo Altemps. The small
is currently undergoing restoration and is therefore not open to the
The matching door on the right, breached in 1940–46 to give a
the so-called "Room of Masterpieces," leads to the epigraphic
The last door on the right wall also dates from this reordering
vestibule, and was made larger than the others to enhance the gre
umental marble staircase leading, then as now, from the ground
the upper floor of the museum. This staircase, which substitute
mer one built in *peperino* and belonging to the priory of the Cart
is remarkable for the quality and variety of its marbles and the m
workmanship of the wrought-iron banister. This leads to the sec
lustrating the proto-history of the Latin peoples. The last bay of
wall before the door shows remains of tempera paintings, probab
the second half of the nineteenth century, composed of a zone of d

and curvy yellow ochre cornice with a pediment framing a *faux* marble door. At the far end of the hall is the sumptuous eighteenth century doorway in marbles and stucco. Two large fluted marble columns support and enhance the imposing and complex framing décor in stucco, with its symmetrical bas-relief seraphim and oval window lighting the vestibule. At the central apex a seraph juts out of a shell in high relief, creating a transition to the volutes which grow with vigorous plasticity from the capitals of the columns. Copious festoons and garlands draping the pediment enrich the composition. Below, a stem with the symbol of the Carthusian fathers superimposes the sober modeling of the door. The door has been attributed to Vanvitelli, who undertook the transformation of the church of Santa Maria degli Angeli in 1749, but the rich plasticity of the decoration, however, seems to indicate the work of one of his students.

Several works of exceptional quality are displayed in the Vestibule, such as the sarcophagus with a Dionysiac procession (1)* from the area of Santo Stefano Rotondo (fig. 34). The statue of the figure in a toga (3) with a non-pertinent head was found in excavations connected with the building of the Ministry of Finance, in the immediate vicinity of the Baths. This is a particularly interesting and amply studied piece, because the juxtaposition of the head with the body seems to have taken place in antiquity. While the lower part is datable to the second century AD, the head is ascribed by the overwhelming majority of scholars to the fourth century AD and identified as Constantius Gallus, half-brother of Julian the Apostate and himself Caesar in the Eastern half of the empire. The herm (4) which follows is only partly ancient; the plaster head, of the Hermes-Antinous type, is a modern integration. This piece was discovered on the grounds of an imperial villa near Castelporziano. The female bust on the opposite wall (6) found during the construction of the Tiber riverbanks is another one of the first pieces to enter the museum. This portrait head of an elderly woman, which, for the hairstyle, is characteristic of the female members of the Severan family and datable to the beginning of the third century AD, was mounted on an older bust from the Antonine period, but in this case, the intervention was recent. The most noteworthy object, both for its historical interest and its artistic qualities, is the portrait of Caracalla as a youth (7) from the House of the Vestals in the Forum. It is an official portrait datable on the basis of comparisons with coins to AD 204.

The landing of the monumental staircase leading to the upper floor displays a draped statue of high artistic quality from Cori. This is a second-century AD copy of a model of Kore deriving from a prototype of the Classical era but with significant contaminations from the Hellenistic period, through which the copyist comes to privilege a frontal view of the figure, which probably, as in similar cases, served as a mount for a portrait head of the imperial family or retinue. [MMC, NP]

* The numbers in parenthesis refer to the numbers of the pieces in the exhibition.

34. The sarcophagus with a Dionysiac cortege

35. The rooms of the
epigraphic section

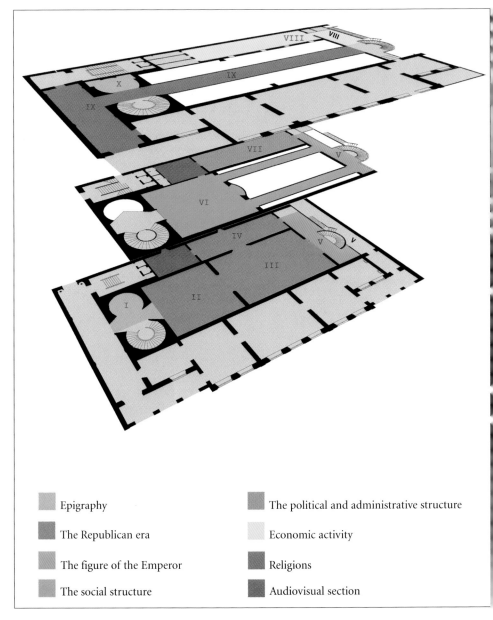

Epigraphy

The Republican era

The figure of the Emperor

The social structure

The political and administrative structure

Economic activity

Religions

Audiovisual section

THE EPIGRAPHIC SECTION

The section dedicated to epigraphs occupies the "Room of the Master-pieces" of the Museo Nazionale Romano, built in the 1920s and ampli-fied in the 1950s. The necessity of consolidating and restoring structures in a noticeable state of decay allowed for the possibility of altering the in-ternal space and creating a new exhibition space conceived for the present display. Taking into consideration the principal characteristics of epi-graphic material, it was decided to install multiple exhibition levels in this hall which previously contained only one floor, by inserting a system of landings in the large central hall culminating in a long glassed-in gallery (G. Bulian, in *Archeologia e Giubileo. Gli interventi a Roma e nel Lazio nel Piano per il Grande Giubileo del 2000*, Naples 2001, pp. 46-49).

The museum's epigraphic section illustrates the birth and diffusion of the Latin alphabet, which is still universally valid, and presents a collection of monuments bearing inscriptions, all the time underlining its indispens-able documentary value for our knowledge of the Roman world. The abundant choice of material displayed was culled from the vast epigraph-ic collection of the museum, which includes some ten thousand lapidary documents and several thousand types of other inscriptions (*instrumen-tum domesticum*) such as brick stamps, ceramic or glass vessels, lead tubes (*fistulae*), stamp seals, slingshot projectiles (*glandes missili*), among others. These rooms dedicated to inscribed communication display around nine hundred pieces, including precious terra-cotta sculptures and various ar-chitectural elements which help to place the written documents in a pre-

36. The central hall

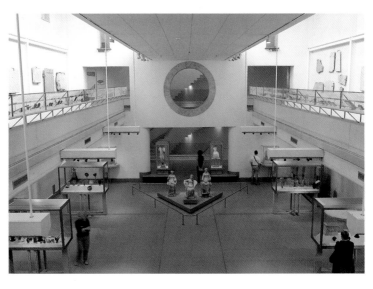

37, 38. Bronze lamp with a support for mounting it on the wall, bearing an inscription containing the names of four dedicators. End of the Republican period

cise architectural context. Room I opens up the exhibition with an introduction to ancient writing, employing documents underlying its general sense and essential lines. The inscriptions follow the advance of Roman civilization from the beginnings of written Latin, and their production seems closely connected with the evolution and development of Rome; the few dozen epigraphic documents of the archaic period grow into several thousand at the end of the Republican era and, finally, into tens of thousands from the Imperial age. The room contains a display laying out a wide typology of pieces, which emblematically represent the various techniques of writing on different supports (figs. 37, 38), the wide variety of content, and the personalities and social forces determining the context of the message. On the corresponding landing above (Room X), the general theme of writing extends to writing instruments and the technique of carving inscriptions on stone, together with a glimpse at other, more rapid means of writing, to give an overall illustration of the prestige of writing in the ancient world. Its revival in the Humanistic age is effectively represented by the inscription dedicated to Pomponius Leto (*CIL* VI, 3477*) by two of his disciples at the Roman Academy, and by two fakes executed by Pirro Ligorio (*CIL* VI, 4*b, 937*).

The exhibition itinerary develops along broadly chronological lines. Room II, dedicated to the Archaic period (eighth–fifth century BC), presents the oldest written documents in Latin, together with other material from the same archeological contexts. Apart from the first alphabetic signs scratched (*graffito*) on objects from the Via Laurentina necropolis (F. Cordano, *Par. Pass.* 36, 1981, pp. 128-134, nos. 1-2), the most noteworthy documents collected here are the terra-cotta fragment scratched with the word *Rex* from the *Regia* of the Roman Forum (*CIL* I², 2830), the metal plaque recording the Dioscuri, Castor and Pollux, which was found in the Sanctuary of the Thirteen Altars near ancient Lavinium (Practica di Mare; *CIL* I² 2833), and the so-called *Lapis Satricanus*, the votive base set up by a group of soldiers (*sodales*) led by Publius Valerius and reused in the foundation of the Sanctuary of the *Mater Matuta* in *Satricum* (*CIL* I², 2832). Among the uninscribed objects the noted panoply of Lanuvium stands out (figs. 39, 40). These arms of a warrior and athlete expert in discus throwing are considered a real rarity in the context of the modest funerary furnishings of the fifth century BC, whose luxury was curtailed by sumptuary laws.

39, 40. Helmet and breastplate from the tomb of the warrior Lanuvium. Circa 470 BC.

The exhibition of the next room, Room III, which covers the middle of the Republican era (fourth-third centuries BC), is arranged along essentially topographical lines aimed at outlining the expansion of Rome, with the consequent formation of *municipia, coloniae latinae* and *civitates foederatae*. The inscriptions and furnishings displayed come mostly from the principal sanctuaries of Rome and Latium. The itinerary opens with a group of finds from the Tiber belonging both to the cult of Esculapius, who was worshipped in a sanctuary on the Tiber island, and to Hercules (*CIL* I², 2443; *MNR* I, 2, II, 34), whose temple was in the area of the Foro Boario. Documents from three nearby cities follow: *Lanuvium*, with the oldest metal-letter inscription, inlaid on a fountain basin from the Sanctuary of Hercules (*CIL* I², 2443; *MNR* I, 2, II, 34); *Lavinium*, whose temple precinct near Tor Tignosa yielded the memorial stone to the Lare (*CIL* I², 2843); and *Ariccia*, from whose territory around Casaletto came the remarkable terra-cotta statues and the busts of Demeter and Kore.

The opposite side of the room displays funerary materials with *graffito* inscriptions from the tomb of the *Rabirii* in *Tusculum*, as well as the votive inscriptions from the *Aphrodisium* of Ardea, the temple of Juno Lucina in *Norba* and, finally, from the temple of Fortuna Primigenia in *Praeneste*, with a famous votive crown in stone (*CIL* I², 1445).

The monuments visible in Room IV illustrate the various social categories which played such a determining role in civil conflict, shaped the late Republican period and led to the formation of a new social and political structure. Following the base of Lucius Mummius (*CIL* I², 2930a), destroyer of Corinth in 146 BC and symbol of a revival of the senatorial order, the contracts for restoration and maintenance interventions on the Via Cecilia (*CIL* I², 808, cf. p. 954) and on several urban streets (*CIL* I², 809), make precise references to the great distributors of public works, members

47

41. Edicola with portraits and an inscription on the rim of the niche.
Second half of the first century BC

of the ever-more-defined Equestrian order. After these are inscriptions recording slaves and freedmen, members of the *ordo apparitorum* (fig. 41) composed of civil servants directly dependent on magistrates, members of the commercial class and artisans and their associations. The far end of the room focuses on the condition of women, represented emblematically by the marble slab dedicated to *Atistia* (*CIL* I², 1206) by her husband the wholesale baker Marcus Virgilius Eurysaces and once placed on the front of the tomb still visible at Porta Maggiore, as well as by the so-called *Laudatio Turiae* (*CIL* VI, 37053), the funerary eulogy of a wife who managed to save her husband and family patrimony during the civil wars.

The last room of the ground floor and the succeeding spaces on the upper floors house inscriptions from the Imperial era, arranged according to the themes of social organization, political and administrative institutions, economic activity and religion. Room V, with the two spaces superimposed near the staircase, is dedicated to the figure of the emperor as supreme exponent of Roman society and apex of power. Here, for the first time, are displayed the bronze base and the large marble case rack dedicated to the Julio-Claudian dynasty, brought to light recently during the course of excavations carried out at the foot of the Palatine hill near the *Meta Sudans* (*CIL* VI, 40334). The theme of the imperial cult provides the context for the slab from the Via Marmorata listing the feast days, with a calendar and the list of magitrates and *magistri vici* (*I. It.* XIII, 12). On the floor above (Room VI), an itinerary unravels from left to right along the landings (including the large space usable as a conference room) presenting documents pertinent to the various classes which formed the pyramid of Roman society. After the numerous fragments attributed to the *Ara Pietatis* (*CIL* VI, 40420-1, 40424-6), inscriptions of a certain importance concerning figures of senatorial rank, such as the funerary inscriptions of the historian Tacitus (*CIL* VI, 1574) and of the consul Quintus Veranius (AE 1954, 4), and of the equestrian order, including the sarcophagus of the young Marcus Aurelius Romanus (*MNR* I, 8, V, 8) with a scene of Ulysses and the Sirens, and that of Julius Achilles (*MNR* I, 1, 187) (fig. 42) with pastoral scenes.

Along the opposite landing, the epigraphic documents refer to the emergent social classes which had some chance of acceding to the higher social classes, including the members of the *ordo decurionum* (components of the local senates in the various cities of the empire), the military, important businessmen, members of the *ordo apparitorum* in the service of the presiding magistrates, and, finally, the freedmen of the emperor.

Room VII is dedicated to illustrating Rome's political and administrative structure, for which epigraphs are the most abundant and precious source of information. A distinction between duties accorded to members of senatorial rank and those typically carried out by equestrians highlights the differences in roles and power in the public administration and the political, judiciary and military spheres. The exhibition opens with the traditional career path of the *cursus honorum* inherited from the republic and continues with the offices created under the new monarchical system, reserved for the highest social order, such as the *praefectura urbana* or the *praefectura alimentorum* instituted by Trajan: for example the very important *tabula* of the bronze *Ligures Baebiani* (*CIL* IX, 1455; *ILS* 6509) (fig. 43). The posts filled by members of the equestrian rank are illustrated by documents pertinent to the offices of the *annona*, the praetorship and the *vigiles*, to which belong the dedication to the prefect of Commodus, L. Julius Julianus (*CIL* VI, 31856; *ILS* 1327) and the plaster fragment with *graffito* from the *excubitorium* of the Seventh Cohort of *vigiles* in Trastevere (*CIL* VI, 3062-65).

The spaces around the stairway on the second floor and in Room VIII offer a brief outline of the commercial activities of Rome's economy through inscriptions relative to the employees of the large warehouses, traders, artisans, farmers and members of other trades and professions, as well as numerous documents concerning freedmen and slaves of both the emperor and private households, whose industry lay at the base of economic life. Particularly interesting are the documents relative to professional associations, which assumed a fundamental role with the advance of the Imperial age. The activities recorded in the epigraphic texts include both those regarded by Cicero as dignified, such as medicine, and those unsuitable for a free man, such as acting, chariot racing or gladiator. The room also offers the visitor the sarcophagus with a representations of dif-

42. Sarcophagus of Julius Achilles with pastoral scenes. Circa *270 BC*

ferent professions (*IG* XIV, 929; *MNR* I, 2, II, 44) and the noted slave collar in a superb state of conservation (*CIL* XV, 7194; *ILS* 8731).

The section arranged along the large landing and in Room IX beyond the staircase illustrates the religions of the Romans both public and private. The dedications to the *Genius* (divine soul), *Lares* and *Penates* (household guardians), and *Manes* (spirits of the dead) allude to domestic cults. The cult of ancestors, practiced also in the Jewish and Christian communities, is evidenced by a choice of stone slabs and inscribed cinerary urns arranged along the length of the gallery. Among these are the funeral eulogy of freedwoman *Allia Potestas* (*CIL* VI, 37965; *CLE* 1988) (fig. 44), the *libellum* (*CIL* VI, 2120 = 32398a; *ILS* 8380) referring to the translation of bodies in a tomb built along the Via Flaminia, and several metrical texts. The Hebrew inscriptions, rich in symbols, record various synagogues and religious offices; the Christian world offers the stele of *Licinia Amias* (*ICUR* 4246), considered one of the oldest documents bearing the symbols of the fish and anchor, juxtaposed with a pagan dedication to the *Manes*. The exhibition concludes with the gnostic inscription of *Flavia Sophe* and several anepigraphic slabs from

43. Tabula alimentaria
of the Ligures Baebiani,
101 AD

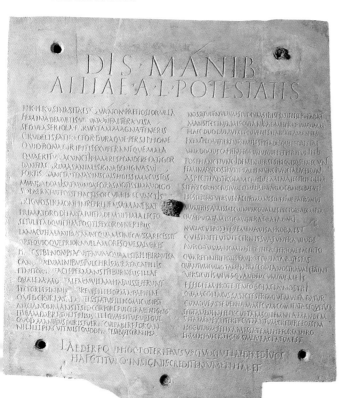

44. *Eulogy of* Allia
Potestas.
Second century AD

45. *Mithras Petrogenitus.*
Second century AD

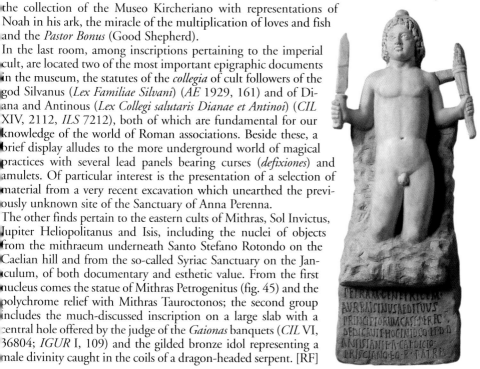

the collection of the Museo Kircheriano with representations of
Noah in his ark, the miracle of the multiplication of loves and fish
and the *Pastor Bonus* (Good Shepherd).

In the last room, among inscriptions pertaining to the imperial
cult, are located two of the most important epigraphic documents
in the museum, the statutes of the *collegia* of cult followers of the
god Silvanus (*Lex Familiae Silvani*) (*AE* 1929, 161) and of Diana and Antinous (*Lex Collegi salutaris Dianae et Antinoi*) (*CIL*
XIV, 2112, *ILS* 7212), both of which are fundamental for our
knowledge of the world of Roman associations. Beside these, a
brief display alludes to the more underground world of magical
practices with several lead panels bearing curses (*defixiones*) and
amulets. Of particular interest is the presentation of a selection of
material from a very recent excavation which unearthed the previously unknown site of the Sanctuary of Anna Perenna.

The other finds pertain to the eastern cults of Mithras, Sol Invictus,
Jupiter Heliopolitanus and Isis, including the nuclei of objects
from the mithraeum underneath Santo Stefano Rotondo on the
Caelian hill and from the so-called Syriac Sanctuary on the Jan-
iculum, of both documentary and esthetic value. From the first
nucleus comes the statue of Mithras Petrogenitus (fig. 45) and the
polychrome relief with Mithras Tauroctonos; the second group
includes the much-discussed inscription on a large slab with a
central hole offered by the judge of the *Gaionas* banquets (*CIL* VI,
36804; *IGUR* I, 109) and the gilded bronze idol representing a
male divinity caught in the coils of a dragon-headed serpent. [RF]

46. Geomorphological map of ancient Latium showing the locations of the principal centers of Latial culture.

■ *Alluvial, lacustrine and glacial deposits, clay-sand conglomerates, clastic and calcareous detritus. Travertines.* HOLOCENE - PLEISTOCENE - PLIOCENE

■ *Sea and continental deposits, chalky sulphur, marly-arenaceous, calcareous-marly and clayey.* MIOCENE - PALAEOCENE

Carbonate deposits, calcareous often rich in flint, marl and clay, dolomites. CRETACEOUS - JURASSIC - TRIASSIC

▨ *Volcanic deposits* PLIOCENE - PLEISTOCENE

1. Rome
2. Antemnae
3. Fidene
4. Pratica di Mare (Lavinium)
5. Ardea
6. Anzio
7. Borgo Le Ferriere (Satricum)
8. Marino
9. Castel Gandolfo
10. Ariccia
11. Grottaferrata
12. Gabii
13. La Rustica
14. Ficana
15. Castel di Decima
16. Laurentina
17. Tusculum
18. Lanuvium
19. Velletri
20. Colonna
21. Tivoli
22. Palestrina

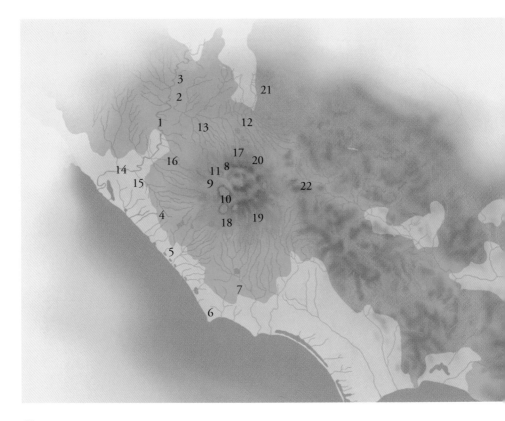

PROTOHISTORY
OF THE LATIN PEOPLES

This new section of the Museo Nazionale Romano, housed in the upper floor of the Michelangelesque cloister, illustrates the development of culture in Latium from the end of the Bronze Age (eleventh century BC) through the Iron Age to the Orientalizing Period (tenth–seventh centuries BC) by means of material from the archeological sites around Rome.

From the point of view of museum conception and exhibitional criteria this section constitutes an absolute novelty in Roman archeological museums, as it does not show pieces from historical collections or excavations subsequent to Italian unity, but exclusively from systematic excavations carried out in the last decades using archeology as a direct instrument of ethnographic and historical reconstruction, with an anthropological approach to the materials and contexts.

The *Latium vetus*, or Old Latium (the territory between the Tiber and Circeo), offers a particularly favorable terrain for archeological reconstructions, as many of the most important complexes have only been brought to light in the last thirty years with systematic long-term excavations, some of which have been published in their entirety.

The study of these important sites has permitted scholars to reconstruct the most important aspects of the communities who lived in the region between the late Bronze Age and the Iron Age: their funerary, social and religious ideologies, socio-political formations, economy, organization of the territory and relations with the nearby regions. The information from the Archaic period which so often remains hypothetical for Rome because of its uninterrupted occupation finds ample contemporary documentation in the regional sites thanks to their systematic excavation and analysis.

The Scientific Project

The context in which the museum presents the objects and archeological information is furnished by the system of contemporary and related material elements which furnish direct information on the community which produced them in a precise moment of its evolution. As a consistent explanatory apparatus is necessary to give the public a clear perception of the information contained in the archeological documentation, the museum has provided visual reconstructions, graphic displays, maps of the overall sites and individual elements, texts and captions for each period, specific groups of objects, while searching to reduce the length of the texts to a minimum, and striving to adopt clear terminology without sacrificing scientific accuracy.

The Display

The exhibition, created to respond directly to the need of communicating the scientific information of the museum, freely uses the walls of the

47. Spatial reconstruction of the crater of Castiglione

rooms, covered projecting panels, to mount the mostly unframed images and texts. Many display windows are quite large in order to provide a sufficiently ample space for all of the representative elements of a single complex.

To the illustrative aids on the walls and inside the display windows is added a guide to the section (*Protohistory of the Latin Peoples*) amplifying the texts accompanying the exhibition. This guide is divided into two sections, responding to two equally important necessities: furnishing a coherent overview of the communities in Latium during the period in consideration, and illustrating the site complexes (in particular residential complexes and necropoli) discovered recently in the territory surrounding Rome, which each have their own proper characteristics meriting a specific treatment.

The General Section

The generalized display furnishes a geographical and historical introduction to the Mediterranean as the context in which Latial culture evolved. Ancient Latium (fig. 46) had strong connections both to Etruria, which borders it on the north, where the powerful political and territorial organization of the great Villanovan proto-cities emerged at the same time as the development of Latial culture, and to Campania to its south, the center of Greek colonization from Ischia to Cuma.

A condensed history of prehistory and protohistory in Latium follows, covering the lower Paleolithic era to the Iron Age, as well as a geological and territorial outline of the region. For the period corresponding to the evolution of Latial culture between the end of the Bronze Age and the Iron Age, there is a synthetic outline of the natural and anthropological context of one of the regional sites, in Gabii-Castiglione (fig. 47), together with information on the primary economy, on the demographics of the communities in Latium, and on the chronology of the establishment and development of social organization and political structures. The transformation of society in Latium during this period is characterized by the passage from egalitarian structures and tribal types of organization in villages, to complex socio-political structures of a patron-client nature which appear in proto-urban and then urban forms.

The process by which scholars have reconstructed the structure and organization of the communities in Latium in their oldest phases is illustrated by two cinerary tombs from the first Latial period (*circa* eleventh century BC), from the locality of Quadrato along the Via Tuscolana (fig. 48) and from the Forum of Julius Caesar, belonging to individuals who filled politico-military and priestly roles and by a chart outlining the primary indicators of social role by gender and age.

48. Furnishings from the male cinerary tomb in shaft 1. Latial Period III, eleventh century BC, Rome, site of Quadrato

Section concerning the proto-historic sites in the territory of Rome

The section concerning the archeological sites displays the two necropoli of the Gabii district (the future Latin city on the Via Prenestina), the necropolis of Osteria dell'Osa and the burial site of Castiglione (fig. 49). The district is centered around the ancient volcanic crater of Castiglione, which still held a lake in the historical period. The first occupations of this area go back to at least the middle of the Bronze Age (second millennium BC). This period saw the establishment of an inhabited conglomeration, probably a village of huts containing several dozen individuals, on the eastern side of the inside of the crater. At the time of this habitation, the crater was filled with a lake or swamp. The subsistence economy was based on the exploitation of natural resources, agriculture and pastoral activities.

49. Aerial map of the Osteria dell'Osa/Gabii/ Castiglione district (by F. Picarreta):
1. The depression of the Osa;
2. The ancient Via Prenestina;
3. The present Via Prenestina;
4. Via di Poli;
5. The necropolis of Osteria dell'Osa;
6. The necropolis of Castiglione;
7. Tomb discovered in 1889 (n° 601),
8. The "tomb of the warrior" (n° 600);
9. The chamber tomb excavated illegally (n° 602)

 Necropoli systematically explored

 Traces of necropoli in the Iron Age

 Isolated tombs

 Inhabited sites in the Bronze Age

 Traces of habitation in the Iron Age
  10: Phase IIB
  11: Period III
  12: Orientalizing period
  13: limits of the Archaic period city

In the first Iron Age (tenth–eighth centuries BC), the rim and part of the inside of the crater housed a series of small habitations with their necropoli. The necropolis of Osteria dell'Osa probably belongs to one of the more important villages, that of Castiglione to a lesser community of shorter duration. In the second half of the eighth century BC, the inhabitants of the villages dispersed throughout the area gathered on the southeast rim of the crater, starting a process of urbanization which led towards the end of the seventh century to the birth of the Latin city of Gabii. The necropolis of Osteria dell'Osa documents the full evolution of a community in Latium between the tenth and seventh century BC, and yields the most ample documentation of the Period II of Latial culture. There are around 450 tombs of this period, separated into groups which probably correspond to the extended families which formed the community. Sev-

eral recurring elements in the furnishings, for example the use of the same type of *fibula* by males of different groups, probably indicate that the various families of the necropolis fell into two main lines of descendance; demographic estimates put the size of the community at no more than a few hundred people. The groups are represented by both sexes and every age. Throughout Period II, both inhumation and incineration were practiced; the furnishings reflect various aspects of the social identity of the deceased closely linked with his or her sex and age.

For this period a large display window in the first room presents a reconstruction of the spatial distribution and characteristics of the tombs of one of the "families" of the community in the northern group of tombs: in the center are located the cinerary tombs of the adult males, with the large vases (*doli*) containing the urn and the furnishings, usually in miniature. Surrounding them are the tombs of the women, children and elderly, who were, on the other hand, buried. Two small display windows present the furnishings from two incinerations of the most important personages in the community: tomb 142, most likely belonging to a priest, as indicated by the presence of a plaster statuette making an offering and a knife; and tomb 185, with an arrowhead probably indicating a military chief (figs. 50-51).

The succeeding phase (ninth century BC) presents exclusively inhumation tombs whose tomb furnishings document the division of roles between members of the community: for example, the activity of weaving, which occurred at home, is carried out by young women. In their furnishings this function is indicated by the presence of a certain number of spindles and shuttles symbolizing the loom. The material from this period demonstrates close and frequent relations between Latium and the southern regions on the Tyrrhenian Sea (Campania and Calabria) most likely mediated by interregional movements of small groups who integrated themselves into the local communities. As an example of this phenomenon, the museum displays the double tomb combining inhumation (483) and incineration (482) from which comes perhaps the oldest inscription in Greek letters found in Italy. This document could indicate a link between the deceased and southern Italy, which was frequented by Greek sailors long before the foundation of the oldest colonies.

50. The furnishings from the male cinerary tomb in shaft 135. Latial Period II, tenth-ninth century BC, necropolis of Osteria dell'Osa

51. The furnishings from the male cinerary tomb in shaft 142. Latial Period II, tenth-ninth century BC, necropolis of Osteria dell'Osa

52. Reconstruction of the furnishings the "tomb of the warrior" (n° 600) in the necropolis of the Osteria dell'Osa

In the third Latial phase (end of the ninth-eighth century BC), the growing contacts with Etruria and Campania produced profound transformations in the social structure, which in the area of Castiglione led to the formation of the urban center of Gabii. Apart from a few scattered tombs we know only one group of tombs from this period isolated in the center of the necropolis (group N). The sixty-five burials in this group are so closely superimposed on each other that in many cases skeletons and furnishings were seriously damaged by even slightly-posterior burials. Evidently, the group identity is here considered more important than the integrity of the individual depositions. This phenomenon suggests the emergence of a family group in the process of differentiating itself from the rest of the community and underlining in this way its unity and continuity; we are probably here at the cusp of the articulation of the community into *gentes* and *clientes* (the aristocratic families and their subordinates) which will typify Latin society in the archaic period.

Toward the end of Period III, we begin to see a few tombs in the necropoli of Latium marked by the presence of exceptional signs of wealth or prestige, direct precursors of the "princely" tombs of the Orientalizing period. These are warriors' tombs furnished with both defensive and offensive armor, metal dishes and a chariot. The furnishings from the warrior's tomb in the necropolis of Osteria dell'Osa, found badly damaged, consists exclusively of arms (helmet, two shields, spear, javelin, sword, axe and pectoral), bronze ware (biconical vase, *patera*, lid) and objects of prestige (*flabellum* palet, small cult chariot) of Late Villanovan style, reconstructed in a large bas-relief display in the exhibition. This tomb documents the presence of a person of high rank, probably a prince originally from Villanovan Etruria, and perhaps from Veii, but completely integrated within the community of Osteria dell'Osa, where he retained the elevated rank he held in his original society (fig. 52).

In the following Orientalizing period (Latial phases IVa-IVb, end of the eighth beginning of the sixth century BC), the tombs testify to the increasing consolidation of this process of social differentiation. In the advanced phase of the Period III and in the early and middle Orientalizing periods (Latial phases IIIb-IVa), several tombs present furnishings of an exceptional richness (tomb 116), and the later Orientalizing period (Latial phase IVb) sees the introduction of collective tombs, probably used by aristocratic families (tomb 62). The tombs of these last phases are few, and are mostly individual tombs of adults and elderly persons. From the second half of the eighth century, the necrop-

53. The furnishings from the young girl's inhumation tomb. Latial Period II, tenth-ninth century BC

54. *The furnishings from the male inhumation tomb n° 49. Latial Period II, tenth-ninth century BC*

olis no longer corresponds to a residential community; probably, as happened with the other communities scattered around the Castiglione crater, some members of the original community who had moved to Gabii continued to be buried in the necropoli used by their communities in the past, thereby extending a form of symbolic control over the territory.

The necropolis of Castiglione, quite close to that of Osteria dell'Osa and contemporary with its oldest phase, is interesting for the differences in material culture and site organization evidenced between two communities in the same district (figs. 53-54).

These tombs in general present a lesser number of ornaments and the pottery is of cruder workmanship. The furnishings are not linked systematically to the gender or age of the deceased. The ritual of incineration is not systematic and, contrary to what can be seen in the necropolis of Osteria dell'Osa, hut urns appear also in female tombs (tomb 74). Thanks to their excellent state of conservation, the skeletons from the Castiglione necropolis yield exceptionally complete data on a number of aspects of daily life during the Iron Age in Latium. Over 80% of the sample is composed of adults with a generally robust physique linked to intense muscular activity. The average height of the men is 166 cm, and that of the women, 158 cm. The most frequent illnesses concern traumas and pathological deformations in the joints, as well as frequent rib fractures. Their diet, largely based on grains and poor in iron, contributed to anemia and dental decay.

The visual aspect of the habitations is illustrated by the documentation of the Iron Age hut from the beginning of Latial Period III (end of the ninth century BC) found and excavated in the town of Fidene. The museum displays the reconstruction of the hut, which was realized to exact scale on the excavation site, showing the internal organization of the spaces and furnishings as well as a choice of pottery. Inside the hut were found the remains of a small feline; its charred skeleton, displayed in the window, is particularly interesting in that it is the oldest known evidence of a domesticated cat found to date in Italy (figs. 55-60).

The near future will see other sections of the museum organized to display the sites of *Crustumerium*, Acqua Acetosa Laurentina, Castel di Decima and Rustica, thus offering a complete panorama of the protohistory of the territory around Rome. [AMBS, ADS]

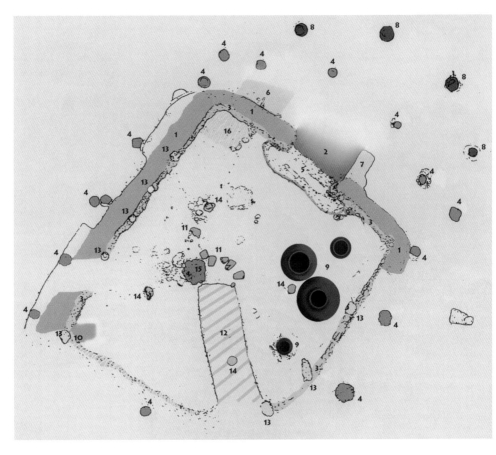

55. Map of the house in Fidene:
1. Altered tufa banquette along the south, west, and part of the north sides;
2. Entry (west side) with porch;
3. Detail of the lower part of the walls in place;
4. Posts along the exterior;
5. Internal space connecting to the entry;
6, 7. Small baked-earth structures atop the banquette on the west side;
8. Posts on the uphill side;
9. Doli from the northern half of the house;

10. The remains of a domesticated cat in the southeast angle of the house;
11. Groups of andirons;
12. Archaic-period trench cutting through the northeast part of the house;
13. Post-holes in the structure of the walls;
14. Internal weight-bearing posts;
15. Hearth in the center of the space;
16. Structure in the southwest angle

56-60. Reconstruction of the house in Fidene

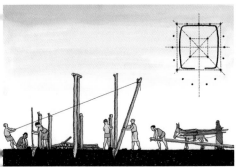 

 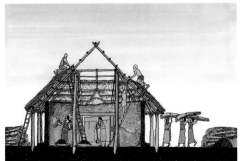

*61. General view of the
cloister after restoration*

THE MICHELANGELESQUE CLOISTER

From the entry vestibule, the imposing eighteenth century doorway gives access to the large cloister of the Carthusian monastery of Santa Maria degli Angeli. The overall effect is highly suggestive, especially given the vast size of the architectural complex (around 10,000 square meters altogether) (fig. 61).

The recent restoration has given back to the cloister its original aspect, distorted by subsequent ochre overpaintings carried out at several times in the nineteenth century which masked the chromatic variations of the plasters and the vibrant treatment of the surfaces.

It is commonly known as the Michelangelesque cloister because of a tradition that attributes the design to Michelangelo, who had in these years projected the transformation of the *frigidarium* of the Baths into the church of Santa Maria degli Angeli e dei Martiri for Pope Pius IV (papal bull of July 27, 1561).

It is probably more exact to say that Michelangelo, who died in 1564, suggested the general plan of the new Carthusian monastery in Rome and that his student Giacomo del Duca collaborated with him on the construction work in the initial phase.

It seems certain, in any case, that the realization of the entire complex followed a unified project and that the work was carried out with great attention and care extending to the decorative details. The restoration has revealed that while the cloister was built in several phases, and therefore with inevitable changes of overseers, the execution was always conducted with extreme accuracy in the choice of the materials and in their finishing.

In spite of its imposing size, the cloister was built in a relatively short period. Begun in 1565, as commemorated by the date carved on the column in the angle near the entrance, it was completed by the end of the seventeenth century.

Because their first priority was to enclose the spaces reserved for monastic life, the Carthusians first put up dividing walls all around the exterior and then proceeded to build the spaces more strictly pertinent to the monastery. Beginning in the angle next to the entrance, they built the prior's residence with its attached garden (first stretch of the southeast Wing I), the small cloister and the large cloister. As the work progressed they added the seven monks' residences on the northwest side (towards the present Via Cernaia) as well as the two on the southwest side, towards the church.

Du Pérac's 1577 map shows the ground floor of the large cloister arcade complete (fig. 62). Only later, as illustrated by Falda in 1676, was the closed upper floor built. Contrary to those who attribute the attic floor to Vanvitelli, the cloister was definitely completed a century before, more precisely in the last years of the seventeenth century, as indicated by a drawing of G.M. Oppenord datable to between 1692 and 1699.

62. The Basilica of Santa Maria degli Angeli and the main cloister in a print by E. Du Pérac, 1577

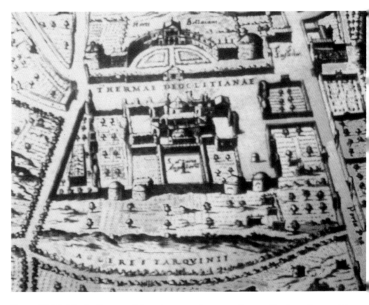

Even if highly influenced by the massive prexistent Baths, the architectural organization of the complex, and thus of the cloister, derives from the monastic rule, and is therefore similar to other Carthusian monasteries in central and southern Italy, although in the Roman cloister the decorative details are willfully simplified and more sober. The designing architect quite successfully reconciles the typological schemes of monastic architecture with the stylistic characteristics of late sixteenth century Roman architecture. The Michelangelesque cloister, as in other Carthusian monasteries, is square, with the surrounding spaces used essentially as a covered walkway; it is also cut off from direct outside communication, and the internal space is laid out in gardens with a central fountain and a cemetery placed near the entrance on the southwest and southeast sides (Wings IV and I) and no longer visible.

On the ground floor, each side is composed of twenty-five bays divided by a total of one hundred monolithic travertine columns of the Tuscan order placed on a continuous molded base, also in travertine, which is interrupted only at the intersection of the principal axes. The architectural and decorative elements of the two levels in the cloister are in *faux* travertine imitating of stone veneer, as was the use in Rome elsewhere, such as in the façades of the Collegio Romano, San Giovanni in Laterano, and the Quirinal Palace. The attic floor, underlined by a high molded trabeation, is rhythmed by pilasters in low relief with a simple projecting block for a capital; the bays in between alternate square and "flattened" oval windows against a background in polished plaster finished in a light "gunmetal" gray (fig. 63). Doors and windows framed by travertine molding open up along the walkways underneath the lunette-pierced vaults. Some of these, perhaps functioning passages for a certain time, are false openings serving to rhythm the long walls. The inappropriate uses of the monastic complex over the course of the centuries (as a military barracks under the French occupation and also as warehouses, an animal shelter, a homeless shelter, a hospital for the blind) altered the space of the cloister without ever adequately utilizing it.

Even though the construction of the Museo Nazionale Romano (1889) involved the removal of numerous later additions to the Baths, resulting

63. Detail of the cloister façade

THE MICHELANGELESQUE CLOISTER

in a more harmonious aspect to the entire complex, the restoration of the cloister, which from the beginning served as a deposit for the works of art discovered in the local archeological excavations, was episodic and piecemeal, mostly aimed at resolving urgent conservation crises or circumstantial logistical problems. The funds made available for the Jubilee Year made it possible to carry out and complete a thorough program of restoration on the cloister, which had fallen into a pervasive state of disrepair. The bulk of the project, which started years ago with the consolidation of the columns and vaults, was brought to completion by June 2000 for the public opening of the museum. Prior to restoring the surfaces of the internal and external façades, historical, iconographical and scientific analyses were carried out to accurately determine the original color of the plaster rendering as well as the techniques used for its realization. The cloister now appears as it did originally, with the polished blue-gray background offset by the stucco decorations in *faux* travertine modeled with the *rigatino* technique frequently used in the period (fig. 64).

The restoration was both thorough and delicate. First it was necessary to remove the nineteenth century layers of paint with two passages of "dry" sandblasting so as to not further damage the already fragile plaster, then a manual cleaning to eliminate the residues of pigment in the grooves of the faux travertine moldings. After the first sandblasting the plaster surface was consolidated, as it was still legible but peeling off of the wall (figs. 65, 66). Specialized restorers worked on the surfaces and decorations with the same care used for a wall with full fresco decoration. Great care was taken to retain all of the original elements possible and to proceed with reintegrations only when strictly necessary and, then, with traditional materials and techniques as close as possible to the original. The works of art displayed in the walkways have all been restored (some on new bases) (fig. 67) and rearranged. Over the course of the last few years, the opening of Palazzo Massimo and especially Palazzo Altemps have entailed the removal of a number of pieces originally displayed in the cloister. This is the case, for example, with the conspicuous nucleus of material from the Mattei collection, which entered the Palazzo Altemps. At the same time, numerous pieces coming from local excavations have been added to the cloister. The arrangement of works in the cloister walkways largely followed the general lines set down in the previous layout. The first two walkways principally present objects of a funerary destination found in the major urban burial cen-

64. *The restoration of the stuccos in* rigatino *technique*

65. The consolidation of the plaster layers

66. The revealing of the original plaster layers

67. The arrangement of the works of art in the walkways of the cloister

ters. These include sculpted portraits of the deceased, as well as altars both celebratory and cinerary, and sarcophagi, which are mostly concentrated in Wing II. This walkway also displays a collection of architectural elements notable for their artistic quality, expression of typology and/or style, or simply the sumptuousness of their marble and stone materials. Wing III, on the other hand, presents a more heteroclite group of objects, ranging from altars and statue bases belonging to the *equites singulares* and altars dedicated to divinities to statues and reliefs from both a funerary context as well as of a purely decorative and private nature, which provides an introduction to Wing IV, dedicated to developing the thematic richness of these genres in the Imperial era. The presentation of these materials, significant for various particular reasons, begins on the right for those coming from the vestibule with the southeast Wing I, and proceeds in a counterclockwise direction with the northeast wing, Wing II, the northwest Wing III and the southwest Wing IV. The individual pieces are identified by a numbered information plates with a brief description in Italian and English. For the commodity of the visitor, the guide refers to the pieces by their identification numbers as displayed in the walkways; this numbering begins anew with each wing.

On the left, near the entrance to the cloister, are paintings in oil, both mural and on canvas, signed and dated 1855 by Filippo Balbi (1806–90). The background of the bay inside the door opening has a representation of a Carthusian monk with a long flowing white beard which an inscription identifies as Fercoldo, the father of Pope Clement IV, who took monastic vows at the death of his wife and died in 1265, and the inside of the wooden door is painted with a set of objects in *trompe-l'œil* (fig. 68).

Wing I

The statue of the man in armor (1)*, discovered along the Via Prenestina, is characterized by the sobriety of its decoration, limited to a Medusa head (*gorgoneion*) in the center of the breastplate. It can be dated to the Julian-Claudian period on the basis of typological similarities as well as the treatment of the breastplate decoration. This statue most probably filled a funerary function (fig. 69).

* The numbers in parenthesis refer to the pieces of the pieces in the exhibition.

68. *Portrait of a Carthusian monk (F. Balbi, 1855)*

69. *Statue of a man in armor from the Via Prenestina*

The two funeral altars from Porta Capena (2, 3) belong to a married couple, M. Natronius Rusticus and Petronia Sabina. She seems to survived the husband and taken responsibility for their shared funerary monument. Very similar both in their decoration and general style, the altars were likely produced by the same workshop and are datable to the Julio-Claudian period. The husband was a Roman citizen, and fulfilled various civic responsibilities as a *scriba quaestorio* (fig. 70).

The richly draped headless female statue (5) was found near the Baths in Via XX Settembre in the area of the Ministry of Defense. It is a copy from the Augustan period of a Greek original of the fourth century BC of the so-called "Orant" type, particularly favored in this period for mounting portrait heads.

The following sarcophagus (6), which comes from a tomb on the Via Aurelia Antica, has a chest decorated with a lively Bacchic procession with centaurs, satyrs, maenads, *erotes* and panthers accompanying Silenus, who lies on a chariot pulled by mules and steered by Pan. The *lid* shows Dionysius at a banquet with Ariadne and the same members of his retinue. This work can be dated to AD 160–170.

The funeral altar of *Caius Tullius Hesper* (9) was found in the noted burial ground on the Via Ostiense at the Basilica of San Paolo, and is remarkable for the violent curse it places on anyone who would violate or

70. Altar of Petronia Sabina

remove the remains of the deceased, who expresses a wish to live long on the suffering body and, once dead, to be gathered unto a place of eternal peace. This dates from the middle of the first century AD.

The funerary altar of *Titus Aspulenus Carellianus* (11) comes from another southern suburban grave site, rather extensive and in use through various periods beginning in the Republican era, near the church of the Nunziatella along an old cross-street of the Via Ardeatina. The altar is densely decorated with a wide repertory of motifs common in funerary art referring to immortality, such as the crown, rams' heads, eagles and the figure in the reclining *kline* pose framed by the garland. General stylistic traits and the epigraphic evidence date the piece to the Flavian period.

The male statue in heroic nudity (13) from San Giovanni Incarico in Frosinone provides an excellent example of a sculptural type particularly appreciated and in fashion in the late Republican era, and used as a mount for portrait heads of emperors or other noted personalities. It derives from a Classicist work of the second century BC, the Poseidon by Melo.

The following female statue (17) (fig. 71), thoroughly covered in rich drapery creating a strong play of lines, was found on the Via Latina near Porta Furba. Deriving from a prototype of the Hellenistic era circa 160 BC, the present copy can be dated to the Hadrianic period by the treatment of the drapery. Her left hand holds ears of grain and poppies, attributes of the cult of Ceres, of whom the subject must have been a priestess, This particular iconography was in fashion in funerary art of the imperial family and important persons in the circle of the court.

The two large seated figures, one male (18) (fig. 72) and one female (21) (fig. 73), come from a large rectangular funerary monument in blocks of tufa discovered along the Via Casilina near Torpignattara. They were set up outside the mausoleum and unfortunately both lack their heads, which must have been portraits of the deceased, evidently another married couple. The stylistic and typological charateristics of the drapery date them to the reigns of Augustus or Tiberius. The female statue is clearly inspired by the *Tyche* of Antioch, a prototype of the end of the second century BC, but mediated through later versions.

The child's sarcophagus a little further on (28) is covered with violent and vivid mythological battle scenes: combats between lapiths and centaurs on the chest, and between gods and snake-limbed giants on the remarkably high *lid*. The piece is also singular in that such themes are rather rare in the decoration of sarcophagi and especially in those of children. The artistic quality is rather mediocre, but stylistic characteristics still allow us to date it to the Antonine period. It comes from Porta Medaglia along the Via Ardeatina.

The figure wearing a toga (31), noteworthy for the accurate rendering of the drapery, rich in naturalistic details, comes from the Via Nomentana, and can be dated to the first half of the second century AD, even if the lack of a head prevents more precise dating. At his feet lies a *volumina*, a symbol of wisdom common to funerary iconography.

The three figures of Silenus (36, 37, 38) from the area of the Baths of Caracalla are telamons—weight-bearing elements in an architectural decoration scheme. Such a use was widespread in Roman art, as can be seen in the many examples used to sustain or decorate fountains. The details of the fat hairy body, the beard, and the face in the more well-preserved example, are rendered with a careful incisive hand. Comparison

*71. Female statue
from Porta Furba*

*72. Male funerary statue
from the Via Casilina*

*73. Female funerary
statue from the Via
Casilina*

with other sculptures of the same type suggests a date between the end of the first and the beginning of the second century AD.

Wing II
This walkway lines up a series of sarcophagi of particular interest both in terms of the variety of decorative and figurative themes they present and in their documentation of a wide chronological and typological panorama of funerary art.

The first two (1, 2) both come from grave sites off the Via Latina. The first (1) is decorated with two *Nikai* in flight holding a crown with the funerary inscription, an iconographical theme clearly inspired by official honorary art. The other motifs, such as the cupidons with the overturned torches and horns of plenty, are more typical of the funerary repertoire. The sarcophagus most likely dates from the late Antonine period, while the epigraph was carved a little later, in the beginning of the third century AD.

The second example (2) belongs to a widespread type, decorated with *erotes* holding garlands of fruit and Medusa heads centered in the remaining spaces. It is datable to AD 140–160, and is by no means the only example of this type present in the cloister (cf. 14).

The cinerary altar (3) which follows comes from the Museo Kircheriano, the original nucleus from which the museum's collections developed. It is interesting for the rich decoration containing all the familiar elements of the funerary repertoire common to this form, including rams' heads, sphinxes, eagles, serpents, roosters and garlands of fruit and flowers which completely invade the space, and also for the dedicatory inscription ascribing it to a freedman of the emperor Claudius who worked as a cash officer in his household. It can be dated to the middle of the first century AD.

The sarcophagus from the Via Casilina (4) presents a wealth of figuration highlighted by two winged genies holding a shield with an inscribed image of the defunct. The ensemble is completed with secondary figures common in funerary art: *Tellus* and Oceanus in the lower register, and the group of the centaur Chiron teaching Achilles to play a lyre at either extremity. Such motifs symbolize the elevation of the soul and the apotheosis of the deceased. Stylistic characteristics of the decoration and, more particularly, of the portrait, indicate a date in the reign of Gallienus (fig. 74).

Of a certain interest, although not of high artistic value, is the sarcophagus with representations of a Dionysiac procession (10), once conserved in Via dei Prefetti. The scene opens with a chariot pulled by centaurs, a theme already seen on an example in Hall I (6) followed by Silenus on a donkey with satyrs, maenads and panthers. Stylistic considerations suggest a date at the end of the third century AD.

74. Sarcophagus from the Via Casilina

Another widespread decorative scheme is illustrated by the example from Ostia (12), which combines the theme of the winged genies holding the *clipeus* with the portrait of the deceased and the theme of the four seasons with all their attributes. The sarcophagus was likely produced around AD 250, but the facial features of the portrait, reworked over a previous portrait, indicate a reuse around AD 270.

The following sarcophagus (15), from a later period, bears a dense decoration centered around the figure of Dionysius leaning on a satyr, surrounded by four allegorical figures with the attributes of the seasons. Due to the stylized rendering of the elongated figures and especially of the hair, it is attributed to a workshop which also produced sarcophagi with Christian themes. Its provenance is unknown, but the dating can be fixed around AD 320.

Another sarcophagus with Bacchic scenes (17) was discovered in the church of Santi Nereo e Achille, located on the urban stretch of the Via Appia. The central scene shows Dionysius descending from his chariot pulled by centaurs and discovering Ariadne abandoned on a rock; the rest of the chest is decorated with the usual members of the god's retinue: satyrs, maenads, Silenus and Pan. Stylistic analysis suggests a date in the period of Marcus Aurelius, between AD 170–180.

A representation of the myth of Medea unfolds across the sarcophagus from Palazzo Caucci (22), which was already renowned in the sixteenth century, as testified by period drawings. The story unfolds in the presence of Jason on the far left, and portrays the principal episodes of Euripides' tragedy—Medea sending gifts to Creusa for her wedding to the hero, Creusa's death, Medea killing her own children, and fleeing with the bodies of her children on a chariot drawn by dragons. The composition likely derives from a Hellenistic painting of the end of the second or beginning of the first century BC with various contaminations from later periods. Stylistic analysis and comparison with other examples with the same myth (one of which is conserved in the large hall of the Baths) suggest a date of AD 150–170.

The sarcophagus decorated with garlands from the area of Via Cristoforo Colombo (23) is fragmentary but still interesting for the powerful tragic masks framed by the garlands upheld by cupidons. The *lid* is decorated with the figures of the four seasons, cupidons and akroterial masks. This type of iconography is rather widespread (see example 2 described above) and stylistic analysis indicates a date of AD 150–160.

A collection of children's sarcophagi (27, 28, 29) of unknown provenance are characterized not only for the reduced size of the chest but also for the predilection of decorative schemes showing cupidons in various activities related to funerary symbology. The first (27), dated around AD 160, presents a lively harvest scene, with a *lid* decorated with cupidons riding dolphins. The next sarcophagus (28) shows a group of cupidons playing various musical instruments in a sort of Bacchic procession. Its stylistic characteristics, even in its unfinished state, suggest a date in the beginning of the fourth century AD. On sarcophagus 29 the cupidons are forging arms, an iconographical scheme also found in another example in Wing III (46). Both are datable to the Antonine period.

The two monumental *kline* tombs portraying the deceased on a funeral bed are particularly interesting. The first (33), which was once conserved in Palazzo Rondanini, shows a reclining man of advanced age holding the bust of a woman, evidently his deceased wife. A cavity carved behind the shoulders of the male figure contained the ashes of both members of the couple, as indicated by an inscription on the now-lost *lid*. Of some importance also for the study of funeral rites and customs, the monument is datable to the end of the first century AD, based on the style of the two portraits. On the second monument (36), which comes from the Via Portuense, a draped female figure reclines in front of a child with its clothes gathered and full of fruit. The details of both the figure and funerary bed are rendered with great care and calligraphic precision. This monument can also be ascribed to the same period.

The architectural element which follows (37) stands out for the singularity of its decoration, inspired by the still lifes of Hellenistic art. This is a marble veneer panel decorated with an oil lamp on a tall stand hung with food of every type—hams, fish, fruit and vegetables—as on a tree of plenty. Its provenance is unknown, and the dating to the Flavian era is based principally on its similarities with a pilaster in the tomb of the Haterii from that period.

The child's sarcophagus in terra-cotta (38) bears a stamped decoration with palmette motifs; the epigraph still conserved on its base identifies it as belonging to the youth *Epaphra*. It comes from the *columbarium* of the Statilii family near Porta Maggiore, which held the remains of slaves and freedmen of this important patrician clan of which Messalina, the wife of Nero, was a member. The sarcophagus can be dated to the first half of the first century AD.

Wing III

At the beginning of the third walkway is a series of altars and votive bases (5-11) dedicated to the *equites singolares*, or bodyguards of the emperor, found in the area of this military unit's barracks in Via Tasso. The dedications refer both to the Genius of the Emperor and to those gods particularly worshipped by the military or associated with the individual soldier's places of origin. They are datable to the second century AD and display long lists of dedicating patrons with the years of their retirement on both the front and sides.

A triangular base (12) found in the work on the Tiber riverbanks is decorated with motifs proper to the cult of Apollo, such as the tripod and griffin. The unusual form, with its strongly concave sides, suggests that it perhaps served as a tripod. It can be dated to the Augustan age, when the cult of Apollo was particularly linked with the figure of the emperor, who was celebrated as a son of Apollo.

The two statues of nymphs reclining on a rocky backdrop which follow (13, 14) were both found in the region of Lazio: one in Roccagorga and the other in Castelmadama. The iconographical type of the reclining nymph was much in vogue during the Imperial era for the decoration of gardens, fountains and *nymphaea*, due to their association with the theme of water. Both works are likely productions of the second century AD.

The two altars from the Via Trionfale (15, 16) were found in an underground tomb and belong to *Minicia Marcella* and her mother *Statoria Marcella*. A letter of Pliny lamenting the premature death of Minicia Marcella places her death with precision to AD 105–6. Her mother, on the other hand, probably died previously.

A small altar from the Via della Giustiniana (18) has its front decorated with the rare myth of Kleobis and Biton pulling their mother's chariot. The sides contain scenes in a much poorer state of conservation and perhaps, indeed, unfinished: the right shows Dionysius near a temple, and the left portrays the myth of Acteon being transformed into a stag and devoured by his own hunting dogs as a punishment for having surprised

Artemis at her bath. The various myths portrayed have no obvious connection with each other.

The small statue of Asclepius (20) portrays the god according to the most widespread iconographical scheme, partially draped in a mantle which leaves the breast exposed and leaning on a long stick around which coils a snake. This modest copy of the Imperial period derives from a prototype of the Hellenistic era.

The two funerary altars which follow (21, 22) belong to the two brothers *Manius Valerius Bassus* and *Manius Valerius Saturninus*, and were found along the Via Nomentana. The similarity of their typological and decorative characteristics suggests that they come from the same workshop. The inscription informs us that while the brothers fought in the same legion and both held the position of *haruspex maximus*, only Bassus held other administrative posts and he was the one who set aside the money necessary for the construction of the brothers' shared tomb. Scholars propose a date for both altars between the end of the first and the beginning of the second century AD, based on the stylistic characteristics and paleographical elements of the epigraphs.

The portrait of a man from Ostia (23) reproduces the slightly corpulent facial features of a no-longer-young man, relaxed and with a focused, reflexive aspect. This is a good example of portraiture from the Trajanic period, datable to AD 110–120 on the basis of the form of the bust as well as the hairstyle and treatment of the hair.

The front side of the *cippus* in travertine (24) shows the Capitoline triad according to a classic iconographical scheme with the gods enthroned in full frontal view, each with his or her own ritual attributes. The other side displays another triad composed of Asclepius, Hygieia and Telesphorus represented as a boy. The memorial stone, probably of a votive destination, is unique in the juxtaposition of the two subjects, but the crude rendering of the modeling in the figures places it in the context of so-called plebeian art, outside of the canons of official art. General stylistic analysis, and especially the treatment of the beard and hair, impose a comparison with the Arch of the Argentarii, suggesting a date at the beginning of the third century AD

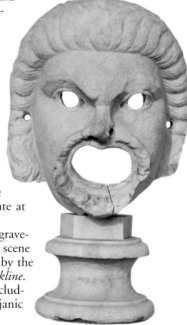

75. *Comic mask*

The comic masks, including the male mask of unknown provenance (30), were used in the decoration of buildings, especially theaters, both outside and inside. This mask can be identified as that of a slave by the presence of the beard around the mouth. Its close similarity to the next mask (36) could indicate that they come from the same building (fig. 75).

The bust in relief of *Aulus Turranius Faustus* (34), unfortunately of unknown provenance, occupies the principal face of a block which formed part of the walls of a sepulchral building, as evidenced by the triglyph sculpted on the right side. The characteristics of the portrait indicate a date at the end of the first century AD.

The cinerary altar of *Julia Capriola* (37) comes from the graveyard on the Esquiline, and is interesting for the banquet scene which occupies the register below the epigraph, enlivened by the realistic detail of the shoes left in disorder at the base of the *kline*. The characters of the epigraph, and a number of details including the hairstyle of the deceased, suggest a date in the Trajanic period.

The draped Aphrodite (38), a Imperial-era copy of a Hellenistic prototype known in various replicas, is a recent acquisition of the Museo delle Terme. Pillaged in 1941 during the last world war, it was given back by the German government thanks to negotiated accords on the restitution of works of art. It is datable to the second century AD.

The funerary relief of the Vettii (43), a family of freedmen, comes from nearby Ponte Mammolo on the Via Tiburtina. Carved in travertine, with a lively but rather crude style, it constitutes an interesting example of popular portraiture and another example of plebeian art, together with the memorial stone (24) described above. The married couple is shown in the foreground holding hands according to the schema of the *dextrarum iunctio*, while the two busts of their children are "suspended" in the resulting background space, a rather common form of representation in this type of production. The present example dates from the beginning of the Augustan age.

The small statue of a sleeping youth with a lantern (44) is a copy of a Hellenistic prototype from the late third or second century BC, an example of the so-called "rococo" style which privileged scenes of daily and family life. Discovered during the work on the Tiber riverbanks near the Ponte Palatino, it remains unclear whether this small genre figure filled a funerary function or merely decorated a garden space. The copy is datable to the first or second century AD.

From the Via Prenestina comes the relief with a centaur ravishing a nymph, perhaps a representation of the myth of Nessus and Deianira (47). An elegant lobed *crater* is sculpted on the right side. The same find also produced a fragment with an inscription permitting its attribution to a funerary monument, which must have been of a certain importance given the artistic quality of the relief. (fig. 76).

76. Relief from the Via Prenestina

Two noteworthy statues in the Archaic style (48, 49) complete the exhi-

bition of this wing of the cloister. The first comes from the Colle Oppio near San Pietro in Vincoli and is a copy of the Artemis of the Trastevere type, datable to the second half of the first century AD. These two works are the fruit of an educated and refined antiquarian artistic conception aimed at reviving aspects of archaic Attic production such as the strong stylization of the drapery with highly decorative and calligraphic treatments. The second statue, of unknown provenance, is datable to the Hadrianic or Antonine period.

Wing IV

The male statue from the Via Flaminia (1) which opens the sequence of works displayed in the last walkway is an unfinished copy (as evidenced by the lack of finishing on the surfaces) of a Classical-period original; the Hermes of Andros, from the school of Praxiteles. The statue almost certainly supported a portrait head, in line with the frequent usage in the Roman era of portraying a subject as a god or in heroic nudity. The prototype is of the second half of the fourth century BC, but the unfinished nature of the present copy makes it difficult to date it with any precision. The small votive altar dedicated to Hercules (2) is decorated on the sides with the representation of a pig, obviously a reference to an animal sacrifice in his honor. The reference in the epigraph to the consulship of the emperor Antoninus Pius indicates a date of AD 140.

The small statue of a girl clutching a dove at her breast (4) was unearthed along together with a number of other statues (cf. 16) in a tunnel built along the Via Prenestina, where they had been hidden. This is a copy from the end of the second century AD of a genre subject typical of the "rococo" tendency of Hellenistic art.

The drunken Dionysius (6) from the Via Cassia is a copy combining aspects of various prototypes all more or less influenced by the art of Praxiteles. The principal models providing the inspiration for the copyist are the Apollo Sauroctonos (killing a lizard with a stone), the Reclining Satyr and the Eros. The fusion of these types most likely occurred in the Hellenistic era. The present example can be dated to the first half of the first century AD on the basis of the fine treatment of the face and the details of the hair.

An unfortunately fragmentary figure of Artemis (7) follows, recognizable by her short chiton and strap to support a quiver, which is, however, missing from her back. The treatment of the drapery suggests a date for the copy in the second century AD, while the original from which it derives is most likely a work of the late Hellenistic era itself referring to models and canons of the fifth century BC, as noticeable in the full frontality of the figure.

Placed next to her is an altar dedicated to the same goddess (8) from the Via Ardeatina, on which she is portrayed as an archer running with her dog. The sides are decorated with a wild boar and a stag with antlers to represent her characteristic forest habitat. This relief reproduces a sculpted prototype of the Classical period in the circle of Praxiteles, and is datable to the second century AD also on the basic of epigraphic analysis of the dedicatory inscription. Another altar (15) decorated with motifs all referring to the hunt and therefore pertinent to Diana, is displayed a bit further on. The two works provide an interesting confrontation of iconographical motifs.

The statue of Apollo (9) comes from a suburban villa and derives its compositional scheme from the Apollo Sauroctonos, a work by Praxiteles which enjoyed immense fame throughout the ancient era and of which there are numerous copies. The present copy, unfortunately mutilated, can still be tentatively placed in the Flavian period on the basis of the treatment of the drapery.

The statue of Aphrodite-Fortuna (10) is recognizable by the small Archaic-style idol and other attributes, such as the cornucopia, the rudder and the globe at her feet. This is a piece of high artistic quality, deriving from a late Hellenistic prototype in which the influence of Praxiteles makes itself felt amid a general eclecticism. The original, probably a cult statue, can be placed in the late second or first century BC, while the museum's copy belongs to the first half of the second century AD.

Harpocrates (11) was an Egyptian divinity, a product of Hellenistic period syncretism, whose iconography was probably created in Alexandria in the third century BC. The god is assimilated both with Heracles and Dionysius, and presents a number of their proper characteristics. The present copy, of mediocre workmanship, comes from a rustic villa along the Via Tiburtina and can be dated with precision, thanks to the context of its find, to the first half of the second century AD.

The female statue (13), a variant of the Borghese Hera type, is an interesting example of a statue intended as a mount for a portrait head. The copyist has in fact greatly privileged a frontal vision of the head. This is a quite valuable work datable to the Flavian period for the transparency and coloristic sensibility in the drapery, deriving from a prototype of the end of the fifth century BC synthesizing the lessons of Phidias and Polyclitus.

The statue portraying an old fisherman (16) has the same provenance as the young girl with a dove (cf. 4), and is also a copy of a "rococo" tendency Hellenistic original. This widespread subject must have been particularly popular with Roman clients; stylistic analysis of the numerous replicas suggests a prototype in the middle of the third century BC of the Alexandrian school which, as seen, privileged genre scenes taken from daily life. The museum's copy dates from the Trajanic period.

The statuette of Fortune (17) from Ostia is identifiable by the presence of the rudder at the base and traces of a cornucopia on the left arm. The prototype betrays the superposition of typically Hellenistic elements on a classical model and was probably created in the first years of the Hellenistic era. The copy from Ostia, on the other hand, should be placed in the second century AD.

The statuette of the elderly woman from Sutri (18) belongs to the same artistic current as the fisherman (16), and this example demonstrates even better the vivid and realistic treatment of details. This is a quintessentially decorative piece, the female counterpart of various figures of shepherds, beggars or fishermen particularly appreciated in the Imperial era for adorning gardens and villas. While the original should be ascribed to the middle of the Hellenistic period in the orbit of the Alexandrian school, the copy, of notable quality, is datable to the end of the first or beginning of the second century AD.

The statue of Ganymede (20), found among the remains of ancient walls along the Via Prenestina, most likely also filled a decorative function in the ambience of a suburban villa. The original which inspired the copyist probably dates from the late Hellenistic period, and might possibly have itself derived from a painting. The violence of the myth is rendered banal by the simple juxtaposition of the scenic elements with no clear connection to the actual rape. As well, the modeling is rather rough. The dating of the work, based on its archeological context, has been placed in the beginning of the third century AD.

The statue of Dionysius (24) is a copy from the Imperial era of excellent quality which originally formed part of a group together with a smaller figure of a young satyr or *erote*, of which traces remain along the statue's left side. The prototype was probably of the Classical period, given the relatively static poses of the figures. The Republican-era villa along the Via Ardeatina in which it was found was altered at various times in the Imperial era and in particular in the Antonine period in which the present statue belongs.

Of unknown provenance, on the other hand, is the statue of Asclepius (27), clearly identified not only by the shape of his mantle, but also by the attributes including the stick, the snake and the Delphic *omphalos*, which alludes to his father Apollo. The copy inspires rather directly from a standard Classical period representation of the god: the cult statue in the sanctuary of Athens, a work by Alkamenes. Still, the copy is hardly of noteworthy quality—once again, a purely decorative intent prevails—and its date remains uncertain.

The altar with the dedication to the Lares (29) from Viale Trastevere is interesting from a historical and antiquarian angle. Framed by a scroll of acanthus and flowers on the front and with a bay tree with birds on the sides, the lively chiaroscuro effects in the rendering of the motifs suggests a date in the middle of the first century AD. The inscription is heavily worn on several lines; what remains is a dedication by the neighborhood magistrates (*vicus*) to the *Lares Augusti*. The abrasions could be the result of an aborted attempt to reuse the piece in a later period.

Also of unknown provenance is the copy of the ephebe (30) of the Westmacott type, so named after the owner of the most significant example, now in the British Museum, itself a copy of the *Kiniskos*, or victor of the juvenile boxing competition, by Polyclitus. Replicas of this work are common and our copy is not one of the best, characterized as it is by a flat and summary rendering of the anatomy.

The series of representations of Hercules which succeed each other in the last stretch of this walkway opens with a copy (31) deriving from an original of the fourth century BC. This rather indifferent and cold piece, encumbered with ungainly supports, dates from the first century AD.

The "sofa" capital (34), generally used atop pilasters or steles, is crowned with a sculptural group composed of two small seated cupidons resting a hand on a bird between them. Behind the bird are the traces of a standing draped female figure. The subject finds comparisons in the "rococo" current of Hellenistic production which, as seen, particularly prized genre scenes. In this particular case, the capital probably formed part of a funerary monument for a young girl. As to the dating, given the scarcity of available elements, it should be no later than the first years of the empire, the period in which the use of the sofa capital dies out.

The statue of the satyr with the goatskin (35) comes from the immediate vicinity of the Baths, being unearthed during the construction of the Ministry of Finance. It is a good example, although unfortunately fragmentary, of the eclectic taste of late Hellenistic art. The statue was utilized as a fountain, as indicated by two holes from which the water must have issued, but it is difficult to find close comparisons even though the figure of the satyr is one of the most popular for this sort of decorative use. The proposed dating is at the end of the first century BC, which is to say the beginning of the Imperial era, a period which saw a notable diffusion of these eclectic works which adopt and reelaborate a variety of iconographical themes in order to provide pleasing and elegant pieces with an almost purely decorative function.

The funerary altar of *Minucia Suavis* (36) found in the Barberini Gardens is notable for the beautiful portrait of the deceased girl. The precise rendering of her still-young features and of her hair indicate a date in the Flavian period, which is confirmed by the epigraphical data. The young girl, aged fourteen, was already married, but the dedication on the funerary monument is from her father.

The statue of Aphrodite of the Callipeges type (38) is a work of the second century AD inspired by work of Callipeges of Siracuse, a piece which itself recalls Praxiteles' Aphrodite of Cnidos and its multiple variants. The present example, notwithstanding its lively chiaroscuro treatment of the drapery contrasting with the modeling of the nude body, is only one of the many replicas in great demand among Roman collectors for its decorative character, and often used to adorn gardens and fountains.

The Medusa head (39) from the angle of a sarcophagus *lid*, on the other hand, is of high value for the chiaroscuro modeling and contrasting surface treatment of the face and unruly hair, whose feral nature is underlined by the presence of intertwined snakes and wings. It has been in fact chosen as the representative image of the Museo delle Terme for its rich symbolic value and its superb quality. Stylistic analysis places it between AD 170 and 190.

An interesting sculpture in the form of a boat (41) serves as a base for a small column. Unfortunately of unknown provenance, it was likely a votive offering for a safe return, as is the case with similar pieces, one of which comes from Ostia. The details of the stormy waves, the decoration of the ship's hull and the balustrade on the deck are all rendered with an attentive and lively hand (fig. 77).

The statue showing Hercules seated on a rocky outcrop and covered with his attribute the lion skin (42) is a recent addition to the museum's collections. Unearthed in the excavation of a suburban villa in Via Carciano at Eusebio, it is datable to the second century AD.

Another statue of a seated Hercules (44) found on the antiquities market presents the god in a different position. Like the statue above, it

77. Votive boat

refers in a general manner to the Heracles of Lysippus which enjoyed great fame in antiquity and spawned a multitude of variants, but it is not strictly speaking a copy. In Lysippus' original, however, the torso is much further back and characterized by a stronger contrapposto, which animates the movement of the arms and legs and gives a strong sense of three-dimensionality to the figure as well as a circular movement, the famous *chiasma* scheme typical of his oeuvre. Our example is of good quality and shows a certain mastery in the execution of the modeling, suggesting one of those Greek artists who worked in Rome in the first century BC for the rich local clientele.

The funerary stele of *Maria Auxesis* (46) from the Via Labicana displays the portrait of the deceased in a niche framed with vegetation. The portrait is quite well done, and successfully renders her thin severe face and lavishly complicated hairstyle typical of the Trajanic period. The inscription reveals that she was a freedwoman and died at seventy-one, an advanced age for the time.

The male statue from the Via Ostia (47) derives from prototypes by Polyclitus, combining them eclectically with typical Imperial era taste. Representing an adult, it is probably a portrait, and can be dated to the middle of the first century AD or shortly thereafter on the basis of the modeling and the type support. (fig. 78).

The center of the garden is highlighted by a large fountain built in 1695, when the work on the cloister was nearing completion. A multi-lobed basin collects the water, which falls from a raised central "cup" supported by dolphins, producing a gurgling jet which broke the silence of the claustral enclosure. Four cypresses surround and frame the fountain. One of these (the oldest) is propped up with an iron ring and a pyramidal support; the other three are substitutes for two trees destroyed in the hurricane of July 18, 1888 and a third tree that died after February 21, 1905. The pieces displayed in the green space of the garden inside the cloister have not been restored or properly arranged. This requires a long-term project inasmuch as they are mostly fragmentary pieces, set on old bases in bad condition. While they need to be rearranged, the general aspect of the space, set a century ago and therefore with its own historical value, will be maintained.

Without going into a detailed description of the many pieces, we would like to present a few of the more important or interesting pieces, arranged around the central fountain (fig. 79).

The magnificent animal heads provide the most characteristic elements of the image of the Michelangelesque cloister, and are what most attracts the visitor's attention, stimulating his curiosity and fantasy. Seven in all (an elephant, a camel, a horse, an ox, a bull, a ram and a rhinoceros), they were unearthed in 1586 during the rebuilding of the palace bought by cardinal Michele Bonelli near Trajan's Column, now the Palazzo Valentini and seat of the Provincial government. They were arranged in the courtyard of the palace, and a sculptor of the period was commissioned to realize one or two animals—certainly the rhinoceros, and possibly also the elephant. The rhinoceros seems to have been inspired by Dürer's famous 1515 etching, which, like all of the master's production, enjoyed great success and was reproduced and copied by many artists even in Italy. The originals were restored at the same time, adding ears, horns and other missing parts and remodeling the horse's mane. With the institution of the museum in the setting of the Baths toward 1890, the statues entered its collections and were set up in the

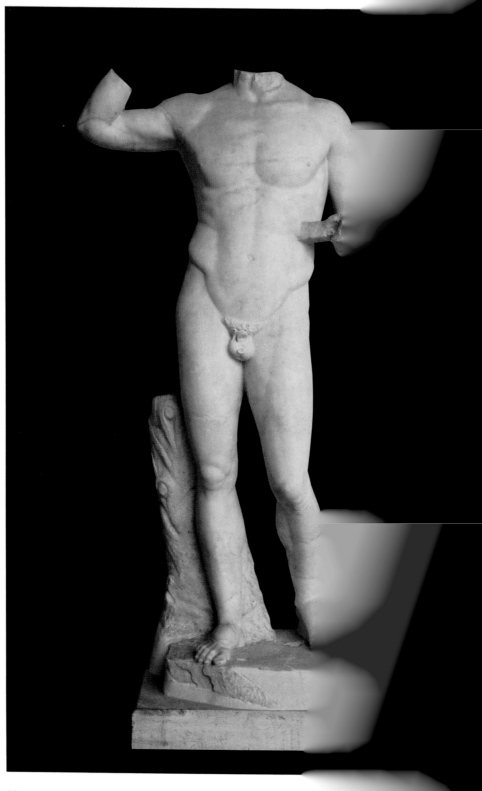

position still seen today. Given their provenance, scholars agree that they belonged to Trajan's Forum, but it is difficult to imagine what their function might have been in the Trajanic complex. Various hypotheses maintain that they symbolize the conquest of Arabia, or imperial policies toward the provinces, or that they are votive offerings (*donaria*) as we know to have been the case with the rams' and bulls' heads placed before the Temple of Vesta. The statues are carved in gray Proconnesian marble, and the care taken in rendering every anatomical detail and the coloristic effects used fit in well with the production of the eastern artists working in Rome in the Trajanic period.

Near the fountain, inside the only flowerbed which is not fronted by one of the heads described above, is displayed a piece of great interest and quality, a fragment belonging to the pediment of a rather small temple. The highly refined figurative decoration shows the upper part of a female figure seen frontally and emerging from a background of lush grain. It is therefore a representation of Ceres, datable by its stylistic characteristics to the beginning of the second century AD. Unfortunately, the data relative to its discovery, which occurred in Via XX Settembre during the excavations for the construction of the Ministery of Finance, are summary and generic and do not permit hypotheses as to its pertinent building. [MMC, NP]

*78. Male figure
from the Via Ostiense*

*79. The fountain
in the center
of the cloister garden*

ARCHEOLOGICAL
ITINERARY

THE HALLS OF THE BATHS

In spite of the serious damage and countless transformations incurred during the course of the centuries, the Baths of Diocletian still conserve important visible remains of the ancient structures. The best-preserved spaces are those in the central block of the complex, but certain structures from the outer wall remain identifiable, albeit in various guises and states of conservation.

As mentioned, a large portion of the central block is occupied by the Basilica of Santa Maria degli Angeli, and this is a logical and appropriate place to begin a tour of the remaining structures of the Baths.

The present entrance results from work carried out between 1909 and 1911 to isolate and renovate the Baths, work which brought about the restoration of the ancient walls and the demolition of a number of later additions, including Vanvitelli's sober façade. The unadorned concave elevation in brick now announcing the church corresponds, therefore, to one of the two larger apses of the *caldarium* (12) of the Baths. Once through the door, we enter into a circular vestibule, easily recognizable as the ancient *tepidarium* (11); the two lateral chapels corre-

* The numbers in parethesis in this chapter refer to the numbers indicated in the plan on page 11.

spond to the two large rectangular exedrae which opened into the room.

From here, we advance to the imposing transept—and in spite of the many modifications brought about in the course of time, the majestic *frigidarium* still retains, overall, its ancient aspect. The church incorporates not only the great *frigidarium* (10) but also two (27a, b) of the adjoining rooms (of which there were six on either side, the remaining ten all being situated outside of the church).

The hall is truly impressive—three vast cross vaults span a transept (the ancient *frigidarium*) 99 meters long, 23.5 meters wide, and 27 meters high, with lower cross vaults covering the lateral spaces.

The eight enormous pink granite columns in the *frigidarium* are left over from the ancient building. Recent studies indicate that these colossal monoliths (13.8 meters tall, with a circumference of over 5 meters) are still in their original location, although with sixteenth century "necktie" bases (*a cravatta*, or a ring of marble fitted around the grooved column and posed on the raised floor, rather than an actual supporting structure). From this we can surmise that the ancient building must have covered just about the same space as the present one. The other eight *faux* marble columns in masonry lining the nave, however, were added by Vanvitelli to match those in the transept, in the process conferring a plastic equivalence to the longitudinal nave of the church.

The church's presbytery, in the area directly behind the basilica, occupies part of the ancient *natatio* (9), breaking up the latter's monumental façade.

Coming back out of the church onto Piazza della Repubblica, and turning right (towards Via Parigi), we can observe, first of all, the monumental access door of the *Olearie*, some of whose rooms are still occupied by the *Società M. S. Reduci Garibaldini* and the "G. Garibaldi" International Institute for Study. Further along the Via Giuseppe Romita, in front of the College of Letters and Philosophy of Rome's Third University (formerly the *Facoltà di Magistero*), we can see fragments of one of the two smaller lateral apses of the *caldarium* (12).

The university building occupies a large sector of the *Olearie*, which was itself installed in part of one of the two wings (13a-15a) flanking the *caldarium*. (The rooms looking onto Via Cernaia now house the Rome Office for the Exportation of Art and Antiquities.) Inside the building, it is possible to reach an internal hallway which corresponds to a portion of the corridor which in ancient times separated the *caldarium* sector from the zone of the *frigidarium* (25a).

Leaving the building, continue along Via Romita until the intersection with Via Cernaia. The remains of the apse walls visible across the street, on the corner facing the beginning of Via Cernaia, correspond to the third (15a) of the four large rooms flanking this side of the *caldarium*; Via Cernaia, in fact, cuts the room in half. Next to these ruins lie the much better preserved remains of the fourth room, known as the Octagonal Hall, or the Planetarium (16a). This hall, together with the adjacent one, which formerly housed the chapel of Sant'Isidoro in Thermis (17a), will be discussed later in detail.

Outside the Octagonal Hall, turning right onto Via Parigi, we can observe, on the right, a good stretch of the northwestern containing wall of the central block, largely restored. The first bit contains the monumental entrance to Sant'Isidoro in Thermis (17a). What follows is the outer wall (restored, and in good part rebuilt) of the three intercom-

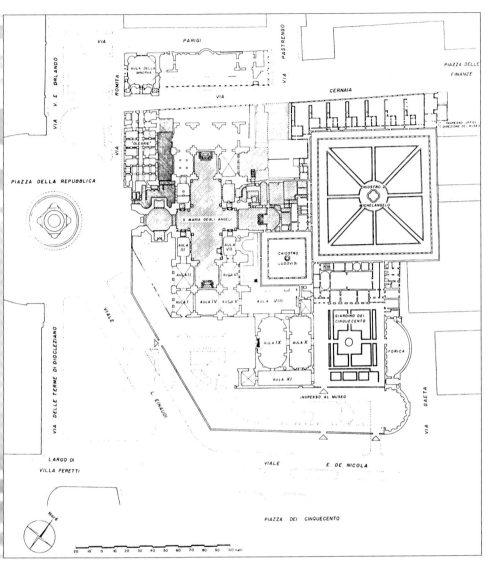

83. General view of the Baths of Diocletian

municating halls which opened onto the porticoed gymnasium on the northwest side of the bath building; the central one is extended on the outside by an apse (18a).

The following ruins belong to another small rectangular hall (19a)—a symmetrical counterpart to that of Sant'Isidoro in Thermis, and, like the latter, also once covered with a cross vault. Next to these are the remains of two of the rooms (20a, 22a) on the northwest side of the *natatio*. In the outer one (20a), located at the intersection of Via Parigi and Via Pastrengo, there is a visible fragment of the original black-and-white floor mosaic, brought to light in 1985.

Turning right onto Via Pastrengo to Via Cernaia and then right again, toward Via Vittorio Emanuele Orlando and Piazza della Repubblica, we can see, on the right, the rooms just described, from the inside. On the opposite side of Via Cernaia, we can make out part of the northwest exercise yard, or *palaestra* (24a), where there are visible remains of

84. External view of the southeast exedra of the tepidarium

85. View of the halls opening onto the northwest palaestra

the previously mentioned polychrome mosaic, and, behind this, the external walls of the rooms flanking the *frigidarium*.

Turning left on Via Giuseppe Romita, past the church of Santa Maria degli Angeli, proceed to the *Museo Nazionale Romano*, which has incorporated various halls of the southeastern sector of the bath complex. Follow the fence surrounding the gardens on your left—the entrance is at number 78, Piazza dei Cinquecento. The gardens more or less occupy the same space as the southeast *palaestra* of the Baths (24b), and the walls behind them correspond to the external elevations of the rooms next to the *frigidarium*.

The great halls of the Baths, after significant restorations to the ceilings, have been used since the end of the 1980s to house several exhibitions of important scientific and documentary value, including, lately, *Italy of the Samnites* and *Rome: Romulus, Remus and the foundation of the city*.

In the next years the museum will proceed with a definitive installation re-proposing works of art which were once displayed in these monumental spaces, but with more adequate criteria for their exhibition, made possible by the restoration, research and reexamination of all these materials thanks to the Jubilee funds.

The rich collection of sarcophagi will find a new space here, and, with

he other sculptural works of funerary nature, will complement imposing reconstructions of funerary monuments realized at the beginning of the last century, such as the tomb of the Platorini rebuilt in
Hall X (21b) for the exhibition of 1911 (fig. 23).

The pieces of architectural decoration and the sculptures belonging to
the great public monuments, both civic and religious, which were unearthed in excavations in Rome's historical center, will add their mon-
umentality to the installations of the other rooms. These include remains from the Temple of the Sun, Valentinian's bridge, the imperial
ustrinum of the Campo Marzio as well as elements from the *Porticus
Maximae*, to name just a few of the more conspicuous complexes represented.

For this reason, we will limit ourselves here to a brief description of the
architecture of the museum rooms (which are those converted for the
1911 Exhibition), following the standard itinerary.

The first seven rooms of the old museum (26b, 28b-31b), together
with the two smaller rooms on the east which once opened into the
frigidarium (10), are arranged around the right wing of the transept of
Santa Maria degli Angeli—which is to say, located between the ancient
frigidarium and the southeast *palaestra*. The entrance to Room I is indicated by a low modern staircase. Most of these rooms (I-II and IV-
VI) are covered with a cross-vault; Rooms III and VII (the two spaces
which once contained basins and opened into the *frigidarium*) have
barrel vaults. The vaulting is partially intact, and the rooms are lit by a
series of variously-sized windows. The side walls occasionally show the
imprints from the original marble veneer.

Room VII exits into an open space, Room VIII (23b), which offers a
partial view of the walls and façade of the *natatio*. The pool area (9) is
now occupied by the smaller cloister of the Carthusian monastery, the
apse of the Basilica of Santa Maria degli Angeli, the sacristy and canonical offices of the church, and other church and/or museum-related
rooms. From this viewpoint, we can see the first two of the five enormous bays which articulated the monumental southwest façade (three

*86. Elevation of the halls
flanking the northwest
palaestra*

rectangular ones and two semicircular, in an ABABA rhythm, framed by projecting colonnades). The central bay, as previously mentioned, is now occupied by the church's presbytery, while the other two are visible from Via Cernaia, or, even better, from Piazzale di San Pio X. All four observable bays show sporadic remains of the original marble decoration (fragments of cornices, brackets and architraves).

Next we enter a large hall, probably an *apodyterium*, or dressing room (Room IX, 22b), situated alongside the *natatio*, covered with a (collapsed) cross vault in the central rectangle and *catino* vaults in the apses at either end (the eastern one is highly restored). On the other side of this room is another large hall (Room X, 21b), this time rectangular in shape, with a partially conserved triple cross vault and wall niches, which seems to have been an entrance hall or lobby for the former. Room XI (20b), which follows, is a rectangular room of uncertain function which closed off the northeast corner of the bath block. At a later stage, it was evidently used as a reservoir; the floor and lower part of the walls still show traces of a waterproof coating.

Room X also gives access to the Museum gardens (the "Gardens of the Five Hundred," after the adjoining Piazza dei Cinquecento), which correspond to a northeastern part of the *xystus*, or *gymnasium quadriportico*, and provide a view of the rather well-preserved façade of Room X (21b).

Across the garden lies the larger of the two semicircular apsed rooms in the northeastern precinct wall, next to the eastern corner. This first room (2b), covered with a vault, presented a colonnade along its concave rear wall, and a facing wall containing niches. An ample, if highly restored, portion of the original black-and-white floor mosaic is still visible, containing both geometric and figurative elements (alternating hexagons and rhomboids, with stylized rosettes in the hexagons) framed with a tress motif. The presence, along the concave rear wall, of bases for some thirty seats, at whose feet runs a small water-channel, has led some researchers to hypothesize that the room was a monumental latrine (*forica*), but it is also possible that it had another function, perhaps serving with the other hall to its right as an *auditorium*, or a space for cultural activities.

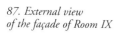

87. External view of the façade of Room IX

*88. View of the
northwest apse
of Room IX*

This other large semicircular exedra (3b), on the northeastern corner of the outer wall, separated from the former by a small rectangular space and a modern metallic fence, retains a greater portion of its vertical structure.

To complete the visit of the remaining visible structures of Diocletian's ancient bath complex, it is necessary to exit the Museum and start along Via del Viminale. On the right side of the street, at number 3 (next to the "Casa del Passaggero"), we can see the naked *laterizio* brick walls belonging to the large rotunda (7b) which was later absorbed into Clement XI's granary.

The corresponding rotunda on the opposite end (7a) is in a far better state of conservation, having been transformed into the church of San Bernardo alle Terme between 1598 and 1600.

To get to this church, whose entrance is at number 94, Via Torino, it is best to retrace our steps a bit, and turn left on the Via delle Terme di Diocleziano, cross Piazza della Repubblica, following the covered walkways, and take the Via Vittorio Emanuele Orlando to the Piazza San Bernardo. This brief walk basically retraces the southwestern side of the outer wall and its enormous exedra.

Entering the church of San Bernardo, we can appreciate how the structure of the great rotunda has remained virtually intact, with the exception that the other three original entrances now accommodate a choir space in the rear wall and an altar on either side. Furthermore, the four semicircular niches in the walls were walled up in the first part of the seventeenth century to make place for eight smaller semicircular openings. The magnificent dome is particularly remarkable—some 22 meters in diameter, and decorated with nine concentric rows of octagonal coffers (32 per row) diminishing upward to a large *oculus*, nowadays closed by a lantern.

THE OCTAGONAL HALL
(PLANETARIUM)

The vicissitudes and transformations of the Octagonal Hall (fig. 5: 16a) in the previous centuries have already been discussed; before proceeding to describe the monument, it is perhaps opportune to give a brief summary of its functions throughout the twentieth century.

Seat until 1911 of the gymnasium of the *Scuola Normale di Ginnastica*, the hall was used during the 1911 Archeological Exhibition to display the French architect Bigot's monumental map of late-Imperial Rome.

In 1913, it was given over to the *Istituto Nazionale di Proiezioni Cine-*

matografiche Educative "Minerva," and rebaptized the *Sala Minerva*. During 1923–25, the space was used to store part of the material from the 1911 Exhibition. In 1925, it was cleared out and converted into a very successful cinema, which, however, was replaced in 1928 by a planetarium (a projecting system capable of faithfully representing and reproducing the movements of the heavenly bodies on a domed screen). The projecting apparatus was housed in the basement of the hall, and the hall itself renamed the Planetarium.

In the following years, there were various interventions on the room's dome, related to its use as a projecting screen, while the *Soprintendenza Archeologica* of Rome tried in vain to expropriate the hall. Only in 1987 was it possible to remove the planetarium furnishings and begin work on a project which included new structural studies of the monument, followed by restoration, and the conversion of the hall into an exhibition space. The present interior, designed by the architect Giovanni Bulian, dates essentially from the year of its completion, 1991, but the steel mesh frame that one sees today on entering the hall, raised up on metallic columns crowned with cast-iron capitals, is what is left of the geodesic dome once used to suspend the planetarium projection screen.

The Octagonal Hall is situated in the western corner of the central bath block, at the end of one of the two wings which, flanking either side of the *caldarium*, formed the southwest side of the building. (The corresponding identical hall on the southern corner has been completely destroyed.) The present-day entrance is on Via Giuseppe Romita, underneath one of the enormous arched windows (the southern one; the window on the west has been walled in) which provided light to the room.

The hall's plan is square on the outside and octagonal on the inside, expanded into the corners by four semicircular apses. It still has its original vault, an eight-lobed umbrella dome with an octagonal skylight at the top, once open but nowadays closed with glass. The extant sixteenth-century graphic documents, in particular several drawings by Baldassarre Peruzzi, show the vault decorated with figurative stuccoes; nothing remains of this vault decoration, nor of the marble and stucco which once graced the walls.

The ancient floor was lower than the present one; the original foundations can be seen in the subterranean structure revealed by the transparent central flooring. The original doors, however, are no longer visible; five in number, they opened into the *xystus* around the western *palaestra*, and the first of the rooms leading to the *caldarium*. One of the previously-mentioned Baldassarre Peruzzi drawings shows a large hexagonal water basin set up in an off-center position in the room. The presence of this basin, the absence of any heating system and the hall's location (between the *palaestra* and the *caldarium*), together suggest that the hall functioned as a secondary *frigidarium* of the bath complex, connected to the nearby western *palaestra*. Recent archeological findings support this hypothesis; in particular, the remains of a *cocciopesto* layer with two superimposed pipes in the northern corner of the hall.

These recent excavations have focused on the spaces underneath the hall, corresponding to the lower floor of the Pauline granary. Three floors of storerooms were in fact installed within the Octagonal Hall, and the original pavement was destroyed either at this time, in 1609, or at the latest around 1640. The planetarium apparatus was

93. Detail of the archeological remains brought to light underneath the Octagonal Hall

originally installed in this basement, accessible by a stairway in front of the entrance. Modern transparent walkways have been installed to permit the visitor to observe the underlying structures, and to get an idea (albeit with some difficulty) of the complex stratification of the site.

The rows of large pilasters in the basement area which support the present floor, lower than the level of the Baths, and also date from the seventeenth century, and again, from either Paul V's 1609 intervention or that of Urban VIII in 1640. The foundations of the bath hall, in brick with masonry reinforcement, are visible along the perimeter. The Diocletian-era structure was built on top of earlier buildings, datable to the late-Flavian era, in brick, concrete, and blocks of travertine. These, in turn, superimpose other structures from the early Imperial era in *opus reticolatum*, in the northeast part of the hall, which align a street with flagstone curbs; this street can be seen immediately to the right at the bottom of the staircase.

The 1957 excavations to the northwest of the hall (underneath Via Parigi) and the 1950 digs in the *fabbricato* (in the courtyard of the building which now houses the Feltrinelli bookstore on Via Vittorio Emanuele Orlando) exposed similar structures prior to the era of Diocletian, and also belonging to two distinct building phases contemporaneous with the Octagonal Hall's ruins. More such buildings are also attested to by the concrete walls underlying San Bernardo and the vast concrete platform brought to light at several points beneath the former Piazza di Termini. This accumulation of contemporaneous finds suggests a surge of peripheral development following

the construction of a large public monumental complex of the Flavian era—perhaps the *Templum Gentis Flaviae*.

Today, the Octagonal Hall of the Baths of Diocletian houses an intimate collection of bronze and marble statues recuperated from the largest bath complexes in Rome (those of Trajan, Caracalla, Diocletian and Constantine), and from the Large Baths in Cyrene, Libya. Their exhibition aims to help the visitor imagine, albeit on the basis of fragmentary evidence, the magnificent sculptural decoration inside the huge Imperial *thermae* of Rome and the provinces.

Some of the statues, in general copies or variants of Greek masterpieces from the Classical and Hellenistic periods, were specially commissioned for the Baths, but most pieces were apparently already in the Imperial collections or acquired at this time, and transferred from their original location in other palaces or monuments.

The most common subjects are gods, heroes, athletes, and mythological subjects, but there were also portraits of poets and philosophers, and honorary statues to historical figures. The statues, it is worth remembering, were almost always painted, and therefore subject to heat damage, so they were concentrated in the unheated spaces: the *natatio*, the *frigidarium*, the *palaestrae*, their adjoining halls, and the libraries—set into niches, apses, and exedrae with metal pinions, or placed on marble bases. A good number were also arranged in the vast open gardens (*xysti*) surrounding the central bath block, as well as in the various structures in the precinct wall: exedrae, *nymphea*, *auditoria*, pavilions.

A number of conventional decorative guidelines determined the disposition of the statues—basic principles of symmetry, of course, but also architectonic relevance. The statues of athletes, for example, were placed in the area of the *palaestra*, and the galleries of poets' and writers' portraits in the libraries or along the tree-lined paths leading through the gardens to these libraries. Often the sculptural decor assumed a propagandistic function—or at the least, consciously expressed broad cultural values.

Given the lack of documentation, it is almost impossible to fully reconstruct the ideological and iconographical program reflected in the sculptural decor, but it is safe to say that it was important that the arrangement coherently and harmoniously articulate the architectonic rhythm. The principles of *ars topiaria* (gardening) also may have been influential.

Two authentic masterpieces from the Hellenistic era take their rightful place in the center of the room: the Hellenistic Prince and the Boxer of the Baths.

These two famous bronzes, cast with the lost-wax process, were found together in 1885 within the confines of the Convent of San Silvestro on the slopes of the Quirinal, in Via XX Novembre. They were apparently reused to decorate the Baths of Constantine, built around AD 315 on the Quirinal in the area between Via XX Settembre and Via Nazionale.

Their common provenance has given rise to a suggestion that the two statues belonged to a group representing the Dioscuri as winners in the

94, 95. The bronze statue of the Hellenistic Prince from the site of the Baths of Constantine on the Quirinal Hill

On the preceding pages:

*96. The bronze statue
of the Hellenistic Prince*

*97. The bronze statue
of the Boxer of the Baths*

*98. The bronze statue
of the Boxer of the Baths:
detail of the hands and
the leather gloves*

*99. Rear view of the
statue of the Boxer; the
sculpted rock seat
is modern*

*100. Side view of the
statue of the Boxer*

boxing contest organized by Amico, king of the Bebrici (with the Hellenistic prince being Pollux, the judge of the contest, and the Boxer, Amico), and that this group evoked the victory of Prince Sylla over Mithridates, King of the Pont. Stylistic and chronological considerations, however, discourage this hypothesis.

The statue of the Hellenistic Prince (also known as the Prince of the Baths, or the Ruler) portrays a youthful and vigorous male with a serious, almost hostile, expression.

The Prince stands with his weight on his right leg and his left leg bent, the right hand posed with the back of the wrist on the right buttock, and the left arm resting on an upright pole (a modern substitution for the original spear). The head, rather small in proportion to the rest of the body, is turned to its right, and the non-canonical facial features (deep-set forehead, high cheekbones, aquiline nose, pointed and dimpled chin and spotty whiskers) are reproduced with a strong realism, suggesting an intended portrait. The rendition of the beard and the short thick curls of hair, finished with a cold chisel, is a true display of virtuosity.

The larger-than-life-size figure is portrayed in "heroic" nudity, and the tone is solemn, regal, approaching the sacred. There is an evident reference to portraits of Alexander the Great, especially a particular model by Lysippus which has him holding a spear.

Scholars generally identify the portrait as a Hellenistic ruler or Roman general of the second century BC, even if other possibilities have not been excluded. There have been recent proposals to identify the statue as either Attalus II of Pergamum before he rose to royal

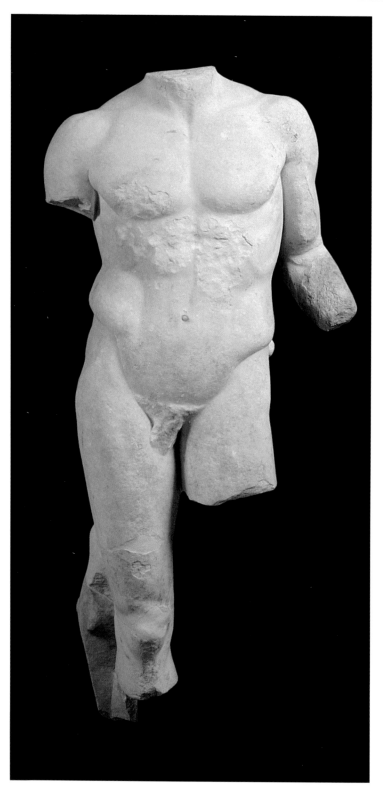

101. Male statue from the Baths of Caracalla. Roman copy from the Hadrianic period of the Hermes by Polycletus from around the mid-fifth century BC

102. *Statue of Herakles from the Baths of Caracalla (most likely from the* frigidarium *of the Baths). Roman copy from the late first or early second century AD of the Herakles of Polycletus from around 430 BC*

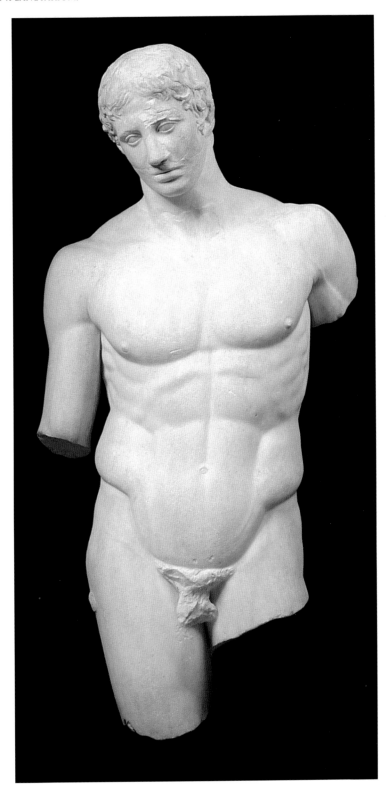

103. Herm in archaic style of Hermes from the Baths of Caracalla. Roman copy from the late first or early second century AD derived from the Hermes Propýlaios of Alkamenes, 450–440 BC

104. Herm of Apollo in archaic style from the Baths of Caracalla (the area between the library and the stadium). Second century AD

105. Male statue of the type known as the Hermes of Andros, from the Baths of Caracalla (the area of the open-air swimming pool). Roman copy from the late first or beginning of the second century AD of a late classical prototype of the school of Praxiteles, 340–310 BC

status—pertinently, the diadem which should indicate a Hellenistic prince is missing, or, on the other hand, the honorary statue erected by Eumenes II of Pergamum in 194 BC in honor of the Roman mercenary general *Titus Quintius Flaminius*. Certain authors have suggested an earlier date, in the third century BC. It seems likely, in any case, to be a work of the Pergamene school, and was probably cast during the first decades of the second century BC.

The Boxer of the Baths portrays an athlete seated on a sculpted rock, with his arms resting on his thighs and hands clasped. (The seat is modern, but something like it was certainly part of the original composition.)

He is nude, although his hands and forearms are protected by *himàntes oxèis*, long lace-up leather boxing gloves with thumb articulations, and doubled fur cuffs.

What is immediately striking is the artist's acute sense of observation, and the crude, almost brutal realism with which he renders the wounds from the just-finished fight as well as those accumulated in the past. Scars of various ages are visible all over the body, but especially on the face: cuts on the cheek and forehead, a broken and deformed nose, cut lip, swollen right eye and ears. Coloristic effects are obtained by using red-copper inlay to indicate the fresh facial wounds and the blood dripped from the turned face onto the right arm and thigh; the original glass eyes have been lost.

The artist's descriptive ability soars to true virtuosity in his meticulous calligraphic rendering of the athlete's tangled curls and body hair, finger and toenails, and especially the gloves. His realism goes so far as to depict an infibulated penis. The athlete appears in rugged condition, with impressive back muscles, even if nascent "handles" indicate that he is no longer young, and the weariness in his face tinges the composition with a certain pathos.

Scholars have proposed an identification of the Boxer with various celebrated athletes of Antiquity, including Polydamas of Skotussa

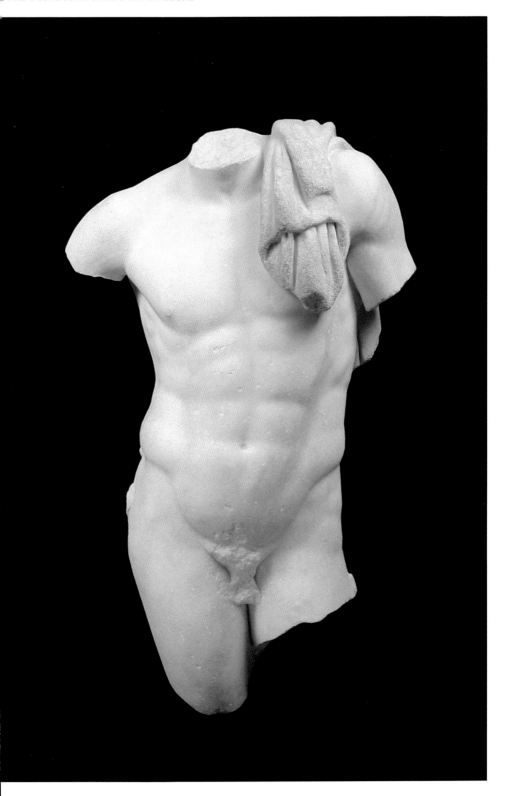

106. Statue of Aphrodite anadiomène (emerging from the sea) from the Baths of Caracalla (the mithraeum underneath the Baths). Roman copy from the period of the Antonines, derived from a famous painting by Apelles (fourth century BC) originally located in the sanctuary of Asklepios in Cos, and later transferred to Rome, where it was placed in the Temple of Venus Genetrix in the Forum of Julius Caesar

and Mys of Tarantum, even though the statue does not seem to betray any clear evidence of being an intended portrait. An old attribution, based on the presumed reading of a signature in the laces of the left glove, gave the work to Apollonius son of Nestor, the Athenian sculptor of the first century BC who signed the Belvedere Torso, but this seems the product of legend, and contemporary scholarship see the statue either as a late fourth century BC work from the entourage of Lysippus, or as a late-Hellenistic production.

Finally, it is worth noting that the surface of the feet and hands is

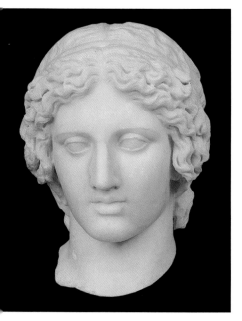 

considerably worn in several points. It is possible that the bronze was once venerated, as is documented in the case of other statues, for the presumed healing powers attributed to it.

The other statues, all in marble, are arranged along the walls. Many of the sculptures exhibited in the hall come from the Baths of Caracalla, built in AD 212–16. Following the order of the exhibition the first statue is a headless male nude, with mutilated limbs, but still recognizable as a copy from the first half of the second century AD of either the celebrated Doryphorus (spear-bearer) attributed to Polycletus, or, perhaps, of a Hermes by the same artist.

Polycletus also provided the original model for the following statue, a copy from the late first or second century AD, also mutilated, representing Herakles in repose, nude and, unusually, without a beard or his usual attributes—probably lacking even his club.

Two herms follow, one representing a youthful Apollo and the other a bearded Hermes. They are both characterized by ornate curled hair-styles, and betray a stylistic affinity with a series of known archaic models of the fifth century BC. The Hermes, in particular, recalls the Hermes *propylaios* by Alkamenes. Both copies are datable to the second century AD.

The beautiful head in marble from the Greek Isles is a copy from the mid-second century AD of another famous work from antiquity: Praxiteles' Resting Satyr, or Satyr *anapauòmenos*, here rendered as an ephebe with thick tousled hair, and crowned with a ring of pine-needles.

The following statue is a very recent discovery (1996) and is also in Greek marble. Although headless and mutilated, one can recognize a woman putting on a short-sleeved *chiton*, tightened around the waist with a belt, usually identified as Artemis, copied in the second century AD from an original of the late Classical or early Hellenistic period.

The following statue is also headless and missing most of its limbs; it is a copy from the beginning of the second century AD of a late Clas-

107. Head of a youth wearing a diadem, from the Baths of Caracalla (the central hall). Roman version from the second half of the second century AD derived from Greek models of the fourth century BC

108. Head of Asklepios from the Baths of Caracalla (the cryptoportico underneath the main axis of the tepidarium*). Copy from the period of the Antonines of a Hellenistic original inspired by the Asklepios of Alkamenes, which also served as the model for the cult statue in the Roman temple on the Tiberian Island*

109. Statue of Apollo "Protector of wolves" from the area of the Baths of Trajan (San Pietro in Vincoli, in a cellar of the School of Engineering). Roman copy from the late Hadrianic age or the Antoninus' period of a Greek original by Praxiteles (fourth century BC)

cal prototype of the school of Praxiteles known as the Hermes of ...ndros.

The next statue is a headless copy from the late second or early third century AD of a Hellenistic original, the Aphrodite *anadiomène* (emerging from the sea), based in turn on a famous painting by ...pelles. The goddess is portrayed nude, having just emerged from the waves, in the act of wringing the water from her hair, and with a dolphin serving to support her left leg.

The other Aphrodite, headless and mutilated in its extremities, is a mid-second century AD copy of a still more famous portrayal of the goddess, Praxiteles' Aphrodite of Cnidos, which shows her nude, standing in a bath, posing her *peplum* on a *hydrìa* to her left.

The next two statues complete the series of works from the Baths of Caracalla. The first, the head of a youth with abundant wavy hair, is a late second century AD version of Greek models from the fourth century BC. The second one is a colossal head of Asklepios (Ascupius) from the end of the second or beginning of the third century AD, derived from a classicizing Hellenistic model.

The remaining statues come from the Baths of Diocletian, Trajan's Baths, and the Large Baths of Cyrene.

The first is a copy datable to the beginning of the early Empire, and a variant type of the previously-mentioned Aphrodite of Cnidos.

The fragmentary statue from the middle of the second century AD, is based on yet another original by Praxiteles, the Apollo "Protector of wolves". The god is portrayed with his right arm on his head and his left arm stretched out in front (originally holding a bow), and a snake winding up a knotted laurel trunk on his left.

A headless and mutilated male bust follows which was carved in the early Imperial era and derives from Greek models of the fifth century BC. The head of the young athlete, is a Hadrianic-period replica in the severe style of the first decades of the fifth century BC, perhaps after an original from the studio of Kritios and Nesiotes, the authors of a famous group representing the Tyrannicides.

Only the base remains of the herm in pentelic marble; it bears the inscription *Q(uintus) Ennius*, identifying it as a portrait of the famous Latin poet. This probably dates from the construction of the Baths of Diocletian.

The Aphrodite of Cyrene, represented by a copy from the first half of the second century AD, is a variant on the Aphrodite *anadiomène*, probably following a version by a late-Hellenistic sculptor of the school of Alexandria in Egypt. The goddess, headless and missing her arms, is here again represented nude, in the act of wringing or arranging her hair, but a dolphin next to her right leg serves as a support for the goddess's *peplum*.

The headless statue of a man in a toga with a bunch of scrolls on the ground to his right dates from the first half of the third century AD. This statue concludes the exhibition. [GT]

THE HALL OF SANT'ISIDORO IN THERMIS

110. Façade of the church of Sant'Isidoro in Thermis, on Via Parigi

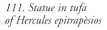

Next to the Octagonal Hall is a smaller, square hall (17a), rather well-conserved, covered with a cross vault whose four supporting pillars are original. The entrance is on Via Parigi, through a portal added in 1754 when Benedict XIV transformed the space into a chapel. The hall had previously been part of the Pauline granary, and in that conversion a dividing wall was added in order to isolate a stairwell.

The church was dedicated to Saint Isidoro the Farmer, a canonized Spanish peasant who was a protector of crops, and called Sant' Isidoro in Thermis. Its dedicatory inscription was fortuitously found in 1990, during the renovation of the hall, and placed back in its original location above the entrance portal. The small chapel, built in the part of the room unoccupied by the stairway, may be the work of Clemente Orlandi; its longitudinal axis was articulated by two arches with stucco decorations, and characterized in the upper part by two visible modifications; two windows and two doors were inserted at the same time as the main entrance.

Today, this façade is all that remains of the chapel, which was demolished this century along with the Pauline staircase. The hall, freed from the accumulation of its later modifications, contains three levels of spaces for exhibitions and conferences.

111. Statue in tufa of Hercules epitrapèsios

112. Herm of a charioteer on a base of bigio *marble. Neronian period*

113. Herm of a charioteer on a base of africano *marble. Flavian period*

The first, set up as a vestibule and exhibition space, is reached by the monumental entrance on Via Parigi. From here, a staircase descends to the second level, which is also accessible by a door which opens on to the archeological area on Via Cernaia. This second level, which corresponds to the (destroyed) floor of the bath hall, houses the permanent exhibition *Sacellum Herculis*, and its flooring is transparent in several places to allow a view of the structures underneath. A set of stairs permits access to this third level, where one can observe walls belonging to the seventeenth century granary, as well as ancient structures in *opus reticolatum* razed for the building of Diocletian's Baths.

The permanent exhibition *Sacellum Herculis* presents the statues recovered from a small cult shrine to Hercules, which was happened upon in 1889 during work for the construction of the Trastevere train station, and subsequently destroyed. The discovery occurred along the present Viale Trastevere, roughly halfway between Piazza Ippolito Nievo and the station, on the eastern slope of Monteverde, in an area once belonging to the *Horti Caesaris*, the very gardens that Julius Caesar bequeathed to the Romans in his will.

The shrine, whose vault had caved in, had been carved out of the tufa, and contained a square niche preceded by two inscribed altars, and a table set on two masonry steps, whose front was decorated with stucco bas-reliefs. The niche was decorated with frescos, and crowned by a pediment with a sculpted relief featuring a club flanked by two vases (*skyphoi*), and, on the underside, a dedicatory inscription: *L(ucius) Domitius Permissus fecit* (*CIL* VI, 30892).

The two altars, one in tufa and the other in travertine, were both crowned with a pediment supported by side columns, and both bear the same inscription: *Imperio. / Herculi sacru(m) / L(ucius) Domitius / Permissus* (*CIL* VI, 30891). All three inscriptions, then, refer to the dedication of the shrine to Hercules—on the god's orders (*imperio*)—by one *Lucius Domitius Permissus*, an otherwise unknown personality who was likely a freedman of the *gens Domitia* living in the first cen-

114. Herm of a charioteer on a base of bardiglio *marble. Neronian period*

tury AD. Among the various pieces recovered from the niche were: two statues in tufa, one portraying a Hercules *epitrapèsios* (sitting down), and the other a Hercules *cubans* (reclining), both from the first century BC; a fragment in *giallo antico* of a head of Hercules, probably from a small herm of the first century AD; and a small terra-cotta bust reworked with gesso which portrays Minerva wearing a Corinthian helmet and the aegis on her chest (first century AD). Archeologists also recovered fragments of the architectonic decoration (capitals, cornices, bits of relief with Dionysiac garlands, etc.), and, at some nine meters from the niche, found a set of seven male herms representing charioteers (this is deduced from the type of robe they are wearing) with busts in *lunense*, or Carrara marble, and bases in various colored marbles: *africano*, *bigio*, and *bardiglio*. Of these seven herms, three appear to be from the time of Nero, one from Domitian's reign, two from the time of Trajan, and one from the Hadrianic period. Two other statues may belong to this group, one in the Musée Royal de Mariemont in Belgium, and the other in the British Museum in London.

The statues and inscriptions clearly indicate a shrine to Hercules within the precinct of the *Horti Caesaris*. The catalogs of the *regiones* (*Cur., reg. XIV*) mention a *vicus* and a statue in the area dedicated to Hercules *cubans*, and it seems likely that this refers to the self-same shrine.

The shrine remained active from the first century BC until at least the end of the second century AD, and probably later (*cf.* the inscription *CIL* VI, 332, which comes from the zone). During the course of the first century AD, *Lucius Domitius Permissus* contributed his own, albeit modest, architectonic and monumental renovation. The presence of the charioteer herms is probably best understood as part of a general hero-worship of the athlete, which involved a syncretic tendency to assimilate and identify him with Hercules. [GT]

117

Bibliography

E. Paulin, *Les Thermes de Dio-clétien*, Paris, 1890.
R. Lanciani, *Ruins and Excavations of Ancient Rome*, London, 1897, pp. 434–39.
R. Lanciani, *Storia degli scavi di Roma,* I-IV, Rome, 1902–04, *passim.*
C. Ricci, "Santa Maria degli Angeli e le Terme Dioclezia-ne" and "Isolamento e sistemazione delle Terme Diocleziane", *Bollettino d'Arte*, no. 3, 1909, pp. 361–72 and 401–05.
P. Guidi and R. Paribeni, "Lavori d'Isolamento delle Terme Diocleziane", *Bollettino d'Arte*, no. 5, 1911, pp. 347–61.
Catalogo della Mostra Archeologica nelle Terme di Diocleziano, Bergamo, 1911.
R. Paribeni, *Le Terme di Diocleziano e il Museo Nazionale Romano*, Rome, 1928.
I. Gismondi, "La sala del 'Planetario' nelle Terme Diocleziane", *Architettura e Arti Decorative*, no. 7, 1929, pp. 385–404.
G. De Angelis D'Ossat, "L'Aula del Planetario ed un disegno di Baldassarre Peruzzi", *Capitolium*, no. 11, 1933, pp. 12–22.
A. Schiavo, *Santa Maria degli Angeli alle Terme*, "Bollettino del Centro di Studi di Storia dell'Architettura", 8, 1954, pp. 15–42.
J.S. Ackerman, *L'architettura di Michelangelo*, Turin, 1968, pp. 272–77.

S. Aurigemma, *Le Terme di Diocleziano e il Museo Nazionale Romano, Rome*, 1970[6].
C. Bernardi Salvetti, "Il sottosuolo delle Terme di Diocleziano nel sec. XVI nei disegni della Biblioteca d'Arte nel Museo di Stato di Berlino", *Studi Romani*, no. 18, 1970, pp. 462–66.
R. Pane, *L'attività di Luigi Vanvitelli fuori dal regno delle due Sicilie*, in *Luigi Vanvitelli*, Naples, 1973.
E. Lissi Caronna, "Roma. Piazza dell'Esedra. Saggio di scavo per la costruzione della metropolitana (February – May 1969)", *Notizie degli Scavi*, 1976, pp. 221–62.
A. Giuliano, ed., *Museo Nazionale Romano*, I, 1, Rome 1979; I, 2, Rome, 1981; I, 3, Rome, 1982; I, 7, Rome, 1984; I, 8, Rome, 1985.
G. Matthiae, *Santa Maria degli Angeli*, Rome, 1982.
Various Authors, *Dalla mostra al museo. Dalla Mostra archeologica del 1911 al Museo della civiltà romana*, Exhibition catalogue, (Rome, Museo della Civiltà Romana, June-December, 1983), Venice, 1983, pp. 11–61.
C. Gasparri, "Sculture provenienti dalle Terme di Caracalla e di Diocleziano", *Rivista dell'Istituto Nazionale d'Archeologia e Storia dell'Arte*, vol. III, nos. 6-7, 1983–84, pp. 133–50.
E. Lissi Caronna, "Roma, Re-

gio VI. Terme di Diocleziano all'interno della Basilica di S. Maria degli Angeli", *Notizie degli Scavi*, 1984–85, pp 207–12.
G. Bulian, in "Terme di Diocleziano-Museo Nazionale Romano: ipotesi di sistemazione dell'area di Via Cernaia", *Roma. Archeologia nel centro* (LSA 6, II), Rome 1985, pp. 508–24.
D. Candilio, "Terme di Diocleziano-Museo Nazionale Romano: scavo nella palestra nord-occidentale", *ibid.*, pp 525–32.
D. Candilio, in A. Giuliano ed., *Museo Nazionale Romano. Le sculture*, vol. I, no. 8, 2 Rome, 1985, pp.435–68.
F. Arietti, D. Candilio, "Terme di Diocleziano", *Bullettino della Commissione Archeologica Comunale di Roma*, no. 91 1986, pp. 358–66.
D. Candilio, "Terme di Diocleziano", *Bullettino della Commissione Archeologica Comunale di Roma*, no. 92 1987–88, pp. 339–41.
U. De Martini, *La certosa di Padula nel sistema delle Certose meridionali*, in *Certose e Certosini d'Europa*, Atti del Convegno alla Certosa di San Lorenzo (Padula, 22-24 September 1988), 1990, pp. 207-217.
R. Pacciani, *Michelangelo, Pio IV e i Certosini a S. Maria degli Angeli, ibidem*, pp. 109–126.
C. Buzzetti, "Terme di Diocleziano", *Bullettino della*

Commissione Archeologica Comunale di Roma, no. 93,
1989–90, pp. 483–84.

D. Candilio, "Terme di Diocleziano. Il prospetto monu-
mentale della natatio", Bollet-
ino di Archeologia, no. 5-6,
1990, pp. 171–73.

M. R. Di Mino, ed., Rotunda
Diocletiani. Sculture decorative
delle terme nel Museo Naziona-
e Romano, Rome, 1991.

L. Nista, ed., Sacellum Hercu-
is. Le sculture del tempio di Er-
ole a Trastevere, Rome, 1991.

D. Candilio, "Indagini ar-
cheologiche nell'aula ottagona
delle Terme di Diocleziano",
Notizie degli Scavi, 1990–91,
pp. 165–83.

G. Bulian et al., "Museo Na-
ionale Romano-Terme di
Diocleziano", Bollettino di Archeologia, nos. 13–15, 1992,
pp. 137–51.

D. Candilio, "Terme di Diocleziano: indagini nell'aula ot-
agona", in Quaderni di Archeologia Etrusco-Italica, 12, 1,
Rome 1995, pp.193–202.

L. Cangemi, Michelangelo e i
certosini a Roma, "Analecta
Cartusiana", 130, Salzburg,
1997, pp. 109-130.

A.M. Bietti Sestieri, A. De
Santis, Protostoria dei popoli
latini. Museo Nazionale Romano. Terme di Diocleziano, Milan, 2000.

R. Friggeri, La collezione epi-
grafica del Museo Nazionale
Romano alle Terme di Diocleziano, Milan, 2001.

Graphic and photographic sources

2, 6, 7, 8, 20, 21, 22, 24, 26, 27,
28, 29, 30, 31, 32, 33, 34, 36,
37, 38, 39, 40, 41, 42, 43, 44,
45, 46, 47, 48, 49, 50, 51, 52,
53, 54, 55, 56, 57, 58, 59, 60,
61, 62, 63, 64, 65, 66, 67, 68,
69, 70, 71, 72, 73, 74, 75, 76,
77, 78, 79, 81, 89, 91, 92, 93,
94, 95, 96, 97, 98, 99, 100,
101, 102, 103, 104, 105, 106,
107, 108, 109, 110, 111, 112,
113, 114: Archives of the
Soprintendenza Archeologica
di Roma.

4: Vasari Archives.

5: from F. Coarelli, Guida
Archeologica di Roma,
Milan 1994².

9, 10: from L. Fornari
Schianchi, N. Spinosa,
I Farnese. Arte e Collezionismo,
Exhibition catalogue (Parma,
Munich, Naples 1995), Milan
1995.

11, 12, 15: Scala Archives.

13, 14: by kind permission of
Adele Amadio.

16, 17, 18: from A. Grelle
(ed.), Vestigi delle antichità di
Roma et altri luochi. Momenti
dell'elaborazione
di un'immagine, Rome 1987.

19: from G.F. Venturini,
Le fontane ne' palazzi e ne'
giardini di Roma, III, table 16.

82, 84, 85, 86, 87, 88:
Vasari photographic studio.

This book was printed for Elemond spa
by Mondadori Printing spa,
via Castellana 98, Martellago (Venice) in 2002